Religion and Medicine · 2

Edited by M. A. H. Melinsky

*Published for the Institute of
Religion and Medicine by*

SCM PRESS LTD

334 01396 8

First published 1973
by SCM Press Ltd
56 Bloomsbury Street London

© *SCM Press Ltd 1973*

Printed in Great Britain by
Northumberland Press Ltd
Gateshead

CONTENTS

PREFACE

This collection of papers which in one way or another have been
given under the auspices of the Institute of Religion and Medicine,
offers some indication, whether by the diversity of their authors or
their titles, of the need and value of trans-disciplinary discussions
on the wide-ranging topics which arise on the frontiers of religion
and medicine. But it displays no shallow optimism. Dr Lambourne
(chapter 3), for example, has some important cautionary words on
the hazards of medical-theological dialogue, and a statistical
enquiry (chapter 15) shows how rigid attitudes have to become
flexible for there to be profitable co-operation. As for the diversity
of the contributors, they include university lecturers in several disciplines, clergy and psychiatrists, a surgeon and a social worker, a
training officer and a theological consultant, a physician and an
industrial chaplain, general practitioners and consultants, a professor and a trade union officer.

But the unity of the book arises not only from the common overall concern of its authors with inter-disciplinary topics on the
frontiers of religion and medicine. For two recurrent threads can
be discerned running through the multi-coloured pattern of the
various chapters.

First there is the claim, explicit and implicit, that the unit of
thinking for medicine and theology must no longer be man as an
isolated individual. Human life, besides having a personal centre,
has a social dimension. To forget that fact is to court disaster
whether we talk of health or salvation, of medicine or the gospel.
Not only must medicine be person-orientated rather than disease-
orientated; a true understanding of persons demands that they are
given a social setting. Here is what Dr Lambourne calls 'the corporate multivariant view of health' (p. 28); here is what is succinctly
expressed in Canon Dillistone's aphorism (chapter 2) that 'the unrelated is the unhealed'. The same point is highlighted in Dr
Courtenay's remark (chapter 8) that pastoral understanding and

medical decisions go together, as in what Dr Mathers has to say (chapter 6) about the role of the pastor as 'a participant member of the flock' (p. 88), a fact which is 'likely to be upsetting to the prejudices of those who have an idea of themselves as shepherds', though they are themselves 'sheep among other sheep' (p. 88). It also arises in a discussion of community care (chapter 10) where it is suggested that 'if medicine is unable to cope with all the problems with which a society is presenting us' then we might have to 'turn to society itself for increasing help' (p. 142).

The second theme that recurs throughout the book is that all scientific enterprise, and medicine in particular, presupposes a conceptual frame. Not only do modern developments in medicine demand a broadening of our concept of medical care (chapter 7); not only does maturity, as Miss Inkster remarks, come from being faithful in every discipline to the vision of an impossible goal, some moral ideal (chapter 5); Dr Lambourne would say (chapter 4) that 'every system of medicine and of medical care has implicit within it a philosophy of personal and political behaviour'. We cannot have a scientific medicine free of social and personal values.

It is because the book is held together by these two presuppositions that it will seem to some to be disturbing. For these two presuppositions are novel enough to call into question familiar roles, expectations and attitudes on the part of doctors and clergy, patients and parishioners, and they carry with them all the hazards of a new perspective, and the searching questions and problems that such a revolution brings with it. Even the question 'What is Man?' (chapter 1) is one which has to be lived with as a perpetual irritant rather than answered in a way which dispenses a soothing bromide. It is in this kind of context that the most practical problems are to be set: problems of abortion (chapter 9); problems of the Samaritan service (chapters 10 and 11) which doctors, we are told, view with attitudes varied from 'an open hostility to amused scepticism' (p. 142); problems of industrial health and how to assist this by making provision within industry for an explicit social purpose, human fulfilment and job satisfaction (chapters 12, 13 and 14).

Not for nothing does the book conclude (chapter 16) with a paper by Dr Michael Wilson on the temptations of Jesus, a paper which shows how theology and medicine can be married in a full and constructive exegesis. Here are temptations basic to humanity, archetypal, not least when we see them as temptations to be less than human, and to avoid those testing relationships in and through which alone we come to maturity. The desire for an authoritarian God; the desire to manipulate men, and the desire to be less than human are temptations for doctor and priest alike. And not a few fall.

It would be so comfortable to settle down into prepared positions on Dr Lambourne's map of distinguishable professional areas in religion and medicine. But the cost of that comfort is to be less than human in medicine and less than reasonable in religion. The value of this book is that it broadens our horizons in medicine and religion alike, opens up new vistas in thought and practice, illuminates contemporary trends and problems, and points us forward to a more humane medicine and a more mature religion. Which is to say that besides being profoundly disturbing, this book is also tremendously encouraging.

IAN DUNELM :
Chairman of Council, IRM

Editor's note

Ian T. Ramsey died on 6 October 1972, the day after handing the manuscript of this preface to the publishers.

1 What is Man?

Roy S. Lee

The Reverend Dr Roy Lee, well known for his book *Freud and Christianity*, is an Emeritus Fellow of St Catherine's College, Oxford. He was formerly Vicar of the University Church of St Mary the Virgin, Oxford, and after that Chaplain of Nuffield and St Catherine's Colleges.

This chapter is based on the presidential address delivered at the Institute's Annual Conference in Norwich in July 1971.

What is man? I must say in advance that I make no pretence to have a final answer, perhaps any answer at all. Rather, I shall concern myself with the posing of the question, with the conditions which govern the search for an answer, and with the need to re-ask the question even when an apparent answer has been found. For my contention is that it is an insoluble question, but one that we are continually compelled to put to ourselves because of the very nature of our being. We are thinking beings and must ask what our relationship is to the rest of the universe. The insoluble character of the question comes from the two ways in which we are bound to frame it and explore possible answers – the objective and subjective. In the former aspect we try to find the answer by considering men in the universe. In the subjective we try to catch our own thinking processes as we participate in the ongoing process which constitutes the actualization of events.

This latter mode of knowledge gives to each of us material that is accessible to no one else. No one can perceive directly as I do what is going on in my mind, and I am cut off from direct perception of the mental processes of everyone else. I may infer and interpret their thinking, and their feeling, from my own experience, and I may even have fuller understanding of it than they have, but I cannot see it as they do. We cannot communicate the quality of direct perception which belongs to introspection. Our words and our gestures, conscious and unconscious, may evoke analogous thoughts and feelings in someone else, but they are then his, not mine. And words and gestures can mislead and be misunderstood.

Every person, then, has two sets of experiences with which to seek an answer to the question, 'What is man?', his inward perception of himself and the common body of knowledge about human behaviour which he shares with other people so far as he cares to dip into it. But the very uniqueness of our so-called subjective knowledge may deceive us – in two ways. First, we are prone to suppose that we know all that goes on in our minds, whereas there is plenty of evidence to suggest that there is much there of which we are unconscious and that these unconscious elements are active throughout our thinking and striving, even if we do not, and, in ordinary circumstances, cannot perceive them. Second, we tend to hold that we perceive ourselves in the act of thinking. This is not so, and I want to emphasize this. What we perceive is the mental activity of the past moment, what we have just thought, not the process of thinking it. In other words, our introspective knowledge of ourselves is also objective, even if its inward quality marks it off from observation by other people. The truly subjective activity remains subjective. I am not sure whether we have what we may call an intuitive awareness of ourselves as mentally active, or whether our knowledge of ourselves as agents is merely an inference, a necessary inference.

We live, then, on three levels. First, the level of subjectivity on which we have only intuitional or inferential awareness of ourselves – that which led Descartes to assert as the foundation of his thinking, *Cogito ergo sum*. Second, there is the intimate area given by introspection, accessible only to ourselves, that which is misleadingly called 'subjective', but which I shall call the introspective-objective. Third is the level of external perceptions, the body of knowledge we share with other people, in which, however, each of us has his unique perspective, determined by his past history and his location in the process of events.

These three aspects of experience belong together as issuing from the same agency. The mode of their togetherness, their co-inherence, is what we seek to understand when we ask the question, 'What is man?'. There is no obvious reason why any one of them should be given priority of importance over the others, but the complexity and the multiplicity of the problems raised by it, in terms of the analysis I have given, exposes us to the danger of over-simplification – so urgent is our need to be able to give some answer. So we tend to omit essential factors from one or other of the levels. The over-simplification takes a variety of forms.

One of the commonest is the religious one enshrined in the soul theory. This stresses the autonomy, and the primacy, of the subjective level, making this aspect of experience into a thing set over against experience, independent, God-given. The inadequacy of this concept was clearly shown by Fr Victor White in his *Soul and Psyche*.[1] We cannot trace any activities of such an independent soul. When we examine our mental processes we find that they are all without exception conditioned, shaped, coloured, directed, by the cumulative effect of our past experiences, of which we are, at any given moment, in some sense a summation. Our thinking is subject to bias, ignorance and illusion. We are not just the makers of our history, we are also its product. So we cannot ignore the specific nature of our experience of the world in which we live.

Simplifications at the opposite pole ignore the subjective aspect and concentrate on what is externally observable or can be conceived as observable by postulating the accumulation of further knowledge and as yet undevised equipment to give us that knowledge. For instance, we assume that every activity of the mind is accompanied by some physical process of the body, especially the brain. There is solid ground to sustain this assumption. The body belongs to the realm of matter and energy, therefore we should be able, in the end, to give a complete account of all the accumulations and discharges of energy which underlie behaviour and gain a complete picture of human life in terms of electrical processes. Perhaps we are not in any great danger of accepting this as an adequate description of man's being, but we *are* at risk when we shift to chemical, bio-chemical, physiological and zoological explanations. Hundreds of thousands of our best scientists are striving to get complete descriptions of the human being in terms of concepts used by these disciplines, and their work beats upon us on every side. Of course such knowledge is invaluable. It becomes dangerous only when we suppose that it gives us a complete picture of man, or when we assume that the particular explanation, chemical, glandular, genetic, or what you will, must be the basic one, determinative or causative of all the others. We should bear in mind the suggestion made by thinkers as far apart as J. B. S. Haldane and A. N. Whitehead that there is a mental concomitant to even the most elementary manifestation of matter. Is it only habit that makes us give priority to matter as basic?

This is not the place to go into the ramifications of these theories and systems which thus purport to explain man. I simply want to draw attention to the reductionism which all too frequently takes hold of those who expound them. The theories give what may be an accurate account of the behaviour of man in terms of physics, chemistry, physiology, genetics, or some other set of principles – including my own favourite study, psychology – but they only explain those aspects which can be measured in terms of their particular concepts. Reductionism comes when other ways of studying man are treated as false or unnecessary, and those aspects of humanity not comprised in the theories are ignored or brushed aside as secondary, derivative.

When the matter is stated simply like that we would all agree that reductionism is a barrier to understanding what man is. But it is my contention that in practice we are, all of us, in some measure victims of it. We pursue different disciplines and within even the same general discipline each of us has his special interests and his special expertise. No one is able to comprehend everything and we are therefore betrayed by our desire for an answer into overlooking the importance of those things of which we know little or nothing, or even into denying that it can have any relevance. And we can cut ourselves off by trying to keep entirely within our own field. We are content with the limited view of man we get from our special field – theology, psychology, medicine, social service, etc., or from some eclectic combination of all. We are convinced that we know the truth, even the whole truth, and we regard as hostile to truth any other interpretation which is based on categories different from our own. What we defend is not truth but the security of our own convictions, or, worse, of our vocations, our vested professional interests.

I want to draw attention just to two ways of safeguarding ourselves from getting into this self-defeating position in which we entrench ourselves in our own limited and thus limiting attitudes. The first is to recognize that those who hold views which differ from ours are of equal or greater intelligence than ourselves. Clearly they see reasons for the conclusions they reach, so there must be some validity in them, even though they appear to deny what we believe to be the truth. The obvious conclusion to draw is that they and we have only partial answers, partial understanding, and they are not opponents denying our vision, but fellow-workers offering further understanding which hitherto we have not had. It behoves us, therefore, to get together with people of other disciplines and other training so that we can exchange views, and by sharing our thinking and striving to find common ground each of us can enlarge his grasp of the truth about man and the universe. Hence the great value of the Institute of Religion and Medicine and similar bodies. We have learned that we gain by sharing practical experience. We have to extend to it the depths of our most precious beliefs.

The second safeguard throws back to what I said at the beginning about the three levels of mental functioning – the external-objective, the introspective-objective, and the subjective. Most of our knowledge is derived from the first area, even about man. It is the area where we can all meet, since it is open to all, so most of our attention is given to it, as things are. The second area has been explored by various branches of psychology, especially the psychoanalytic schools. Because the methods available to work in this area necessarily differ from those which can be used in the external-objective area, those who rely on the latter are often disinclined to allow validity to the methods of psychoanalysis. The behavioural psychologists are strenuously trying to find ways of bringing their study into line with the non-introspective sciences, but they are simply building up new sciences which are complementary to, not destructive of, any sound knowledge gained through psychoanalysis. The latter has, however, shown us that introspection does not of itself give us full or reliable information about our minds. But it has made clear that our minds take shape as a result of interaction between ourselves and our environment as we grow. Our subjective activity, the third level of being, is conditioned by this experience and thus we find all three levels participating simultaneously in mental activity. To ignore any one of them is to falsify the nature of human existence.

It would be a fascinating exercise to examine the function of the body in this interdependence of the three levels of being, but I have to be content with mentioning it without pursuing it. I must end by making clearer what I see as the second safeguard against closing our minds. From the external-objective sciences we learn that man is a product of the universe. It follows, therefore, that the study of man must reveal something of the character of the universe. From the second level we see him shaping as well as being shaped by that universe. The third level – the unobservable subjective – shows not merely that man has become conscious of himself, but also that the universe – for man embodies the universe

– attains self-consciousness in him. The subjective as well as the objective is part of the order of being that we call the universe.

Thus the third level links man with the whole mystery of being. If it is ignored in the effort to find an answer to the question, 'What is man?', we are certain to go astray. Equally we go astray if we isolate it from the other levels of being. On the one hand man cannot be separated from the detailed processes of the universe; on the other he derives his nature from what is its essential nature or its central pattern – what some of us mean when we speak of 'God'. Because our knowledge of the phenomenal world and of God must always be incomplete, any assertion we make about what man is must always be false because it is inadequate. Yet we must go on trying to find a fuller answer or we cease to be men.

NOTE

1. Victor White, *Soul and Psyche*, Collins & Harvill Press, 1959.

2 The Unassumed is the Unhealed

F. W. Dillistone

Canon F. W. Dillistone, formerly Dean of Liverpool (1956–63), was Fellow and Chaplain of Oriel College, Oxford from 1964 until his retirement in 1970.

The chapter here printed is a shortened form of the closing address given at the Annual Conference of the Church of England Hospital Chaplains' Fellowship held at Somerville College, Oxford in July 1969. It owes much to a stimulating re-interpretation of the patristic formula by Professor M. F. Wiles in an article with the same title as this one which appeared in *Religious Studies*, vol. 4, 1968–9, pp. 47-56.

This chapter is reprinted, with some alterations, from the *Anglican Chaplain*, vol. 8, No. 28, 1969, by kind permission of the Editor.

One of the most striking statements to emerge from the Patristic period of Christian thinking is that which forms the title of this chapter. Coined by Gregory Nazianzen, it can only be interpreted within the general context of late Hellenism and its world-outlook. Two spheres were fairly sharply defined – the upper world of light and purity and spirituality; the lower world of murk and contamination and materiality. Within the upper sphere it was possible to conceive of the existence of a divine nature; within the lower sphere the existence of human nature. Divine nature was in all respects perfect and not subject to mortality; human nature was held fast within the enveloping sphere of darkness, disease and ultimate death.

Within such an overall world-view the crucial question which was bound to be asked was: How can human nature be released from the imprisonment within the dungeon of its materiality and mortality? How can it be cleansed from the contamination which entombment within the flesh necessarily entails? And the Christian answer, spelled out in a variety of ways, was: Only by the divine nature immersing itself in the human situation, and from within the situation *cleansing* human nature, *immortalizing* human nature, *transfiguring* human nature, *exalting* human nature – only in this way could man be restored and sanctified. But further it was held that this immersion must be complete: every aspect and activity of human nature had to be *assumed* by the divine if healing was to be effected.

This conviction gains clear expression in the works of Gregory of Nyssa. He writes:

> It was in keeping with his ultimate union with our nature that he should be united with us in all our characteristics. Those who wash off dirt from garments do not leave some of the stains and remove others, but from top to bottom they cleanse the whole garment of the stains, to give it a consistent character and a uniform brightness with the washing. It is the same with our human life, which from beginning to end throughout was stained with sin. The cleansing power had to penetrate it entirely.... That is why the power which amends our nature had to touch the beginning and extend to the end, covering all that lies between.[1]

Given the general world-view of Neo-Platonism and the conception of human nature as a kind of substance in which all shared, the affirmation that *the unassumed is the unhealed* seemed an indisputable conclusion. But with the transition to a different world-view in the scholastic period of the Middle Ages, this basic principle took on a new form. If we read Anselm's 'Cur deus homo?' we find ourselves in a very different system of ideas and language-forms. Now the picture is of a supreme over-lord, who has the right to expect complete deference and loyal obedience from his subjects. His laws are perfect, and while they are observed all is healthy and harmonious. But in point of fact man has failed to give God the honour due unto his name, and has actually broken the laws which he has established. How can such a situation possibly be remedied? It is impossible to imagine that God could allow any structure in his universe to remain disordered (*inordinatum*). In other words, in Anselm's view, *the uncorrected is the unhealed*. Somehow the debt must be paid. Restitution must be made. This principle is applied to the work of Christ, and its implications are worked out for the mediatorial function of the church and its ministers. No man could be restored to health of body or mind if his offences against God had not first been corrected and annulled. A whole system of belief and practice took shape largely as an expansion of the fundamental principle that 'the uncorrected is the unhealed'. Christ had not only lived a perfect life, thereby correcting all of man's grievous errors. He had also died a totally undeserved death, and thereby had brought into being a treasury of grace sufficient to provide remedies for all the disorders and sicknesses of human souls.

But there was to come another major change in the world-view of western man. This was more complex – the result of many new experiences and discoveries – but it emerged as what we generally call the scientific world-view. God was still acknowledged, but in a more remote way as Creator and Sustainer of the universe, while men and even inanimate things had greater possibilities of going their own way. It was useless for man to come to his world with ready-made theories and plans. He must explore, examine, experiment, and thereby gradually build up a body of knowledge about the laws governing the behaviour of the constituent elements of the world of nature and the world of humanity.

So began an era of constant extension and expansion of human *experience*. The self-confidence of the individual grew as he learned more and more about the actual operations of his world, actualities which were often very different from the theories and assumptions inherited from the past. And this held good within the life of religion and art as well as in the realms of the science of the natural world and of the human body. So a new form of the basic principle of my title came to be accepted. I should express it thus: *The unexperienced is the unhealed.*

Some of the greatest advances in medicine were made in this period by pioneers who were ready actually to test in their own bodies the effects of a certain drug or a certain serum or vaccine. They observed and experimented, not only in hospital and laboratory, but also in plague-stricken areas and where disease was rife. So, too, missionaries and evangelists went out into areas of darkness and wretched human conditions and tested, both in their own experience and in the experience of others, the power of the gospel to save. Theology sought to show how Jesus had in fact entered fully into human experiences, accepting temptation, dependence, disappointment, suffering, as he acquainted himself with the human lot. Increasingly it came to be accepted that 'the unexperienced is the unhealed'. Following Jesus, both the pastor and the physician sought to discover the true condition of the individual patient, and to bear witness to the way of salvation – for as Tillich has pointed out, in basic meaning salvation *is* healing.

Is there finally any translation or transformation of the basic principle which seems more in keeping with the new world-outlook of the twentieth century? I suggest that the most striking of all advances made in this century has been in the field of communications. Our world-picture is no longer that of myriads of atoms or of individuals existing like disconnected points in a vast empty space. Rather it is of a vast system of inter-connected energy-events in which new relationships are constantly being effected and in which no part is entirely independent of the rest. The human body has been described as a communications system: the brain is a marvellous communications system: and these are infinitesimally small within a universe which forms an unbelievably expansive network of communications links. In such a universe the most serious threat is a break-down of communication. The whole health of any enterprise depends upon the smooth link-up of its constituent communication potentials.

Within such a framework, the simplest re-formulation of the basic principle seems to be *the unrelated is the unhealed*. Modern theologians have used such phrases as, 'Real life is meeting', 'God's presence is realized between man and man'. A truly personal relatedness is seen as the highest desideratum whether between man and man or between man and God. Alienation, disconnectedness, is seen as the root of all evil: free communication, relatedness as the secret of all good life.

There was a time when theological scholarship was much concerned with 'kenosis' doctrines – what it could mean to affirm that the Son of God emptied himself: also with doctrines of Jesus' consciousness – how far he was conscious of and consciously accepted the necessity of his passion and death. These concerns are, I think, less prominent today. It is doubtful how far such questions can be answered in any detail. But the larger concern now is to determine how Jesus *related* himself to the cultural conditions and social needs and aspirations of his own time: the significance of the particular language-forms which he used and the particular actions which he performed. Through the communications system within which he was enmeshed, Jesus related himself to the human situation of his own time: through a continuing communications-process potentially with the people of all time. But to realize this potentiality is the never-ending task. And within that task the person-to-person, utterance-to-utterance relationship holds the place of supreme significance.

As long ago as 1933 Sir Farquhar Buzzard wrote these words: 'The most important difference between a good and an indifferent clinician lies in the amount of attention paid to the story of a patient.'[2] To listen, to relate, to speak – all are included within the process of communication. And it is by relating theological speech to the presence and power of God operating through the communication channels of which we have become increasingly aware that we can perhaps promote that health or wholeness that men so greatly desire.

Different ages have different conceptions of the way the universe is constituted and of the nature of its apparent imperfections. It is not surprising therefore that the way of healing tends to be expressed through forms of language and imagery appropriate to the diagnosis of the root source of the world's ills. This does not imply that earlier formations of the healing process must be entirely discarded. It does mean, however, that the focus of concern in any particular age needs to be that of bringing the possibility of healing and wholeness into the human situation through the use of methods and paradigms which belong to men's general understanding of the nature of the universe in their own time.

NOTES

1. Gregory of Nyssa, *Catechetical Oration* 27, quoted by M. F. Wiles, 'The Unassumed is the Unhealed' in *Religious Studies*, vol. 4, 1968–9, p.51.
2. Quoted by Robert Cope, *The Quiet Art*, E. and S. Livingstone 1952, p.105, from *The Lancet*.

3 Towards an Understanding of Medico-Theological Dialogue

Robert A. Lambourne

Dr Robert A. Lambourne was a Lecturer in the Department of Theology at the University of Birmingham. This chapter began as a brief lecture to the Royal College of General Practitioners in London in 1969. It was expanded for a meeting of the Institute in London in 1971. Its present form is a working paper for the Sixth Congress of the Association Catholique Internationale D'Etudes Médico-Psychologiques, to be held in Luxembourg in July 1972.

Dr Lambourne died suddenly on Easter Day 1972, soon after preparing this chapter for publication.

The point which I wish to make in this chapter is that the world of medical psychology today is pluralist and that the world of theology today is also pluralist. Therefore any conclusion which follows from an interrogation of the faith by medico-psychological science will be related to which two of the many societies of knowledge were in the first place chosen to be the partners in the dialogue. If we accept this then it follows that we should be alerted to the likelihood that those persons who are highly motivated to take part in such a dialogue may unthinkingly select two societies of knowledge, which not only have much already in common but also have in common congenial assumptions which are mutually unrecognized and therefore uncritically accepted by both parties in the dialogue. This is not, of course, to say that such a dialogue is not of value but it has at least three dangers:

1. Those engaged in the dialogue may overlook the fact that they only represent one small society of knowledge within the pluralist society which their profession constitutes. (Scrutinize the membership of conferences engaged in medico-theological conversation; where are the experimental psychologists, the surgeons and the more traditionalist theologians?)

2. In coming closer together in conference the medical psycho-

logists and theologians may draw further apart from the representatives within their own profession of other societies of knowledge.
The established rules of the conference dialogue may just exclude
a priori the majority of doctors and theologians together with the
distinctive knowledge they should contribute.

3. The dialogue may, without it being fully realized, become
gradually a monologue because the weaker partner only contributes to the dialogue ideas which are recognizably analogous to
those congenial to the stronger partner's position.

A survey of the literature of the medico-theological debate of
the last thirty years will, I believe, support the three contentions
just stated. Nearly all of it is based upon a dialogue between a
subsection (psychoanalysis) of a small section of medicine (psychological medicine) and a subsection of theology (existential theology). Again, my personal experience is that whenever I declare an
interest in a medico-theological dialogue it is invariably assumed
that my field of concern is either 'spiritual healing' or pastoral
psychology based upon medical psychotherapeutic knowledge. But
this is to exclude at least ninety per cent of medicine! The same
literature referred to above also often demonstrates how often the
end result of dialogue is less the mutual enrichment of the two
parties than the capitulation of one to the other. For example,
many books and articles on pastoral theology are empty of a
distinctive contribution from the theological side which has forced
a change in medical thinking.

In this post-Freudian and post-Marxist era we have become
accustomed to the notion of the relativity of systems of knowledge
and their constituent facts. This notion has been universalized of
recent years, its application no longer being confined to so called
'non-scientific' systems of knowledge like theology but extended to
those disciplines like pure sciences of which it had been previously
assumed that they dealt with facts that had meaning in themselves
apart from the thought systems to which they contributed. The
psychology and sociology of knowledge supports the point of view
of those who believe that there can be no complete separation of
facts from values within a body of knowledge and that as a consequence the theological critique of a body of knowledge is not to
be confined to that part of it which explicitly deals with values
but is equally concerned with the hidden values within the body
of knowledge. It is also now appreciated that modern industrialized societies are pluralist with multiple systems of knowledge and

values which, with the ever changing diversity of social organisms based upon different technologies, gives our culture inadequate time to produce a universal body of knowledge and values. This pluralism is found even *within* the societies of medicine and theology. As a consequence there cannot be *one* dialogue between medicine and theology but there must be *many* dialogues. Moreover the distance between the points of view of different bodies of knowledge within the one discipline is not necessarily any less than that between the two different disciplines! We may not *feel* this to be true, but this is because of the psycho-sociological unity of the professional bodies and not because of a rational unity. If, for example, we only select two of the many divisions within each profession and begin our dialogues with (*a*) a surgeon, (*b*) a psychoanalyst, (*c*) a Barthian theologian and (*d*) a Tillichian theologian then there are six pairs of people asking questions of each other – *ab, ac, ad, bc, bd, cd*! Each of these four (*a, b, c, d*) along with the professional bodies which support them have distinctive key ideas about what is basically man's predicament, how basically he can be delivered from his predicament, and what basically are the qualities of a whole, healthy, perfect, saved, man. These basic assumptions we will call a 'deliverance model'.

All human perceptions, because of our biological nature, tend to be shaped by the struggle for survival, and thus by our desire to escape from pain and move towards pleasure. (This is neither to assert a total determinism nor to neglect the possibility that man's final pleasure is happiness in the presence of God.) Thus those systems of knowledge, feeling and action, which like medicine, theology and social work, are intimately concerned with man's personal happiness, tend to organize themselves around the particular dramatic events which have brought deliverance from pain and discovery of pleasure. These key deliverance events give rise to central concepts of the nature of the basic predicament from which man must be delivered and to central concepts of the basic elements of man's health, wholeness or salvation. These three elements constitute a deliverance model. Such a deliverance model is thus constituted of three key concepts :

The concept of 'disease' 'badness', 'sin' etc.	shapes ←	The nature of deliverance experienced by individual	shapes →	The concept of 'health', 'goodness', 'salvation' etc.

The technology of deliverance and the language by which its

nature is explained to the self and to others thus tends to shape the implicit anthropology of the person and community. (Within Christian theology there is a similar tendency for soteriology and its institutionalized forms to determine christology.)

Here are three very crude illustrations of deliverance models:

1. Because of the chronological precedence within medical science of morbid pathology and histology, and because of the early successes of surgery, disease came to be thought of as a focalized unambiguous defect in an individual body. Healing was thought of as the extirpation of unambiguous focal defect from an individual body. Health was thought of as the absence of unambiguous focal defect in an individual body.

2. In cultures where individuals are crushed by poverty and saved by acquiring goods, man's essential predicament may be seen as his own poverty, his healing as acquiring capital for himself, and his wholeness as having his own possessions. Wholeness is understood to be wealth.

3. In a culture influenced by Victorian attitudes to sexuality men may experience liberation by being permitted to verbalize about instinctual drives in the security of a permissive personal environment. Alienation can then come to be thought of as a state of sexual repression. Deliverance is then thought of as being heard without condemnation, and fullness of life is defined as a maximal expression of instinctual drives compatible with self-respect and cultural advance. Here are then three deliverance models:

Badness	*Deliverance*	*Goodness*
Focal defect in an individual	←Extirpation →	Absence of focal defect within an individual
Poverty	←Acquisition of capital→	Possession of goods
Repression of instinctual drives	←Verbalization in an→ accepting personal environment	Appropriate expression of instinctual drives

It must be stressed that these deliverance models structure perceptions of reality and encode a system of facts to make a body of knowledge held by a particular person or society without the participants necessarily being aware that their knowledge is being encoded by a deliverance model and that they are building their science upon a partial consciousness of the reality which is about them. The end result so far as it concerns us is diverse professions built up around diverse techniques and bodies of knowledge each having at its centre a different deliverance model. Deliverance

models may of course affect each other and the three given above
are in their turn dominated by the more basic deliverance model
illustrated below.

We can now understand the manner in which much of our
dialogue between medicine and theology is conducted. One of the
societies within pluralist medicine and one of the societies within
pluralist theology find that they have sufficient in common to
begin to listen to and learn from each other without too much
pain. What still troubles them is their differences and these differences largely spring from the fact that one group uses secular
language and the other uses transcendental language. Their
theoreticians get to work and demonstrate analogies between certain secular and certain transcendental terms in their respective
vocabularies. They thereby build up on the unexamined area of
agreement which first brought them together. The end result is a
sense of unity, leading to an increasing approximation of their
technologies and professional language, and this in its turn leads
to the discovery of fresh analogies in their respective professional
languages. It only needs time if there is a great disparity between
the social status of one profession and the other before the stronger
absorbs the weaker. (Did the pastoral counselling movement prepare the way for a popular 'death of God theology' or the latter
prepare the way for a pastoral counselling movement indistinguish-
able from the secular psychology with which it had been in
dialogue?) *The great fault of this process is that neither side may
see that it is the very things which they had in common at the very
beginning of their dialogue which are the most questionable
assumptions of all.* So, for example, the pastoral psychology movement was based historically upon a deliverance model held in
common by most psychotherapists and many Protestant ministers
within the pietistic tradition. This deliverance model can be crudely
represented thus:

Badness	*Deliverance*	*Goodness*
Appertains to the individual. Is the most striking reality of all. Demands maximum attention. Is unambiguous in its badness and need for eradication.	Is by the individual in his weakness leaving his personal and natural environment and bringing his badness in himself to a profes- sional person in place set apart in order for his badness to be removed.	Is the absence inside an individual of unambigu- ous badness.

This deliverance model, crudely described, owes much to protestantism, capitalism and empiricism in their less admirable forms. Today's pastoral psychology is still based largely upon the coalition of sacred and secular mirror images of that same deliverance model. This coalition is largely possible because the sacred profession is ready to capitulate under the pressure of secularism.

To illustrate in a rough manner the pluralism of medicine and therefore the range of dialogue possible and desirable between medicine and theology the concepts map of medicine which follows is given to stimulate thought. Each of the squares on the concepts map represents one of the societies within pluralist medicine. (Upon each of them a distinctive clinical pastoral education could be based. A catholic clinical pastoral education would need to take account of them all and a lot of other things as well!) Each square on the concepts map represents the basic conceptual deliverance model of a body of professional men with their habitual self-image, techniques and supportive body of knowledge. For example, that square where the unit of context is the individual and where the dominant model of healing is the isolation and extirpation of focal badness represents the deliverance model of surgery and pastoral psychology in the 1950's to which we have made reference above. Each square represents a different deliverance model and thus a different starting point for a medical-psychological interrogation of the faith.

In the present general dissatisfaction with the structures and practices of medicine our attempts to find and adhere to a strategy for reform may be frustrated by the complexity of the facts and the multiplicity of the proffered remedies. It may therefore be useful to represent some of the issues in a scheme which will demonstrate some of the concepts of healing which are striving for recognition or dominance and show the relationship between them. The concepts map below is very tentatively offered to help in this way, not as a determinant of thought but as a stimulant to reflection. It is hoped that it will be taken seriously, but not too seriously!

It will be seen that the vertical North-South parameter indicates the *extensiveness of the unit of context within* which one particular type of caring, curing or health enhancing person, be it doctor, nurse, teacher, minister of religion, or other person, predominantly operates. By 'extensiveness of the unit of context' is meant much more than a shift from an individualistic clinical approach to an epidemiological and demographic approach. What is being indicated is how much of the total environment available for perception is characteristically made the framework of perception of disease and of measurement of healing by that health worker in his routine practice. From South to North the extensiveness in-

	Disease ERADICATION e.g. Surgeon	Disease MANAGEMENT e.g. Physician	CARE FOR (of) e.g. Nurse / e.g. Nature Conservation	LEARNING by stress e.g. Immunologist / e.g. Therapeutic Community	NURTURING existing strengths e.g. School teacher / e.g. Eugenist / e.g. Positive health cultivation	CREATING new styles of being (healthy) e.g. Social visionary / e.g. Humanist biological evolutionist / e.g. Religious genius	
	+ +	+ +	+ +	+ +	+ +	+	COSMIC e.g. W.H.O. visionary / e.g. Process theologian / e.g. Political utopian
	+ + + + +	+ + + +	+ + +	+ +	+ +	+	NATIONAL–POLITICAL–ECOLOGICAL e.g. Adviser to developing country
	+ + + + + + + +	+ + + + + + + + + + + +	+ + + + + + + + + + + +	+ + +	+ + +	+	NEIGHBOURHOOD e.g. Health visitor / FAMILY e.g. General practitioner
	+++ +++ +++ +++ +++	++++ ++++ ++++ ++++	+ + + + + + + +	+ + +	+ + +	+	WHOLE PERSON e.g. Hospital psychiatrist
	+++ +++ +++ +++	++++ ++++ ++++	+ + + +	+ + + +	+ + +	+ +	SYSTEMATIC e.g. Physician / BODY ORGAN e.g. Surgeon
	+ + + +	+++++	+ + + +	+ + +	+ +	+ +	MICRO e.g. Microbiologist

Variable extensiveness of context in which concept operates

Different dominant concepts of what 'healing' is

$\overset{+}{{}_+}{}^+$ Shows concentration of effective concepts used in most present medical education

creases from *molecule,* to *cell,* to *organ of the body,* to *family,* to *community,* to *country,* to *cosmos.* Examples of doctors operating predominantly in these different units of contexts are, moving Northwards, the molecular biologist, the specialist surgeon, the psycho-somatic medicine consultant, the general practitioner, the community orientated psychiatrist, the medical officer of health, the ecologist in a team advising a developing nation, and a medical philosopher envisaging a cosmic utopia.

The horizontal parameter is concerned with those different concepts of what healing essentially is, each of which can dominate a particular professional identity and shape the ideology of medicine which evolves around it. Successively from East to West are *eradication of disease isolated from its unit of context, management of disease in a unit of context, care of a unit of context, assisting a unit of context to learn from stress, nurturing existing strengths in a unit of context*, and *creating new ways of being a unit of context*. Here are some examples:

Isolation of disease in itself from a unit of context with a view to its *eradication* is the dominant concept of healing of a cancer surgeon where an organ of the body is the unit of context. It is also the dominant concept operating within a community unit of context of a doctor planning the eradication of leprosy from a population by mass pharmacotherapy. The consultant physician working in hospital exemplifies the dominance of the concept of healing as *management* of disease in a context. The disease is still the focus of attention and its personal context is recognized but only because it is a factor which must be taken into account for the disease's successful eradication. The dominance of the concept of healing as *caring* for a unit of context, where caring is the necessary activity and curing is a good but not essential aim or satisfaction, is well represented by the traditional nurse where a person is the unit of context and by a parish priest where a community is the unit of context.

Examples of the concept of healing as helping the unit of context to *learn* strengths through stress are, at body level, the physician withholding antibiotics to encourage the development of resistance and, at neighbourhood level, a crisis oriented community psychiatrist.

Examples of professional workers with identities based substantially on the concept of healing as *nurturing* existing strengths are an immunologist where the body is the unit of context, a school teacher where the child is the unit of context, and a community social worker or health oriented general practitioner where the neighbourhood is the unit of context. It is noteworthy that these last professional persons only give secondary attention to defects since their main attention is on how existing strengths can be cultivated. For this reason they will feel tension in themselves with that professional identity built up on the concept of healing as the detection and eradication of defect which was typical of clinical medicine in the 1920–60 period and is still very strong in education for medical and social work today. This is even more so for those people whose activity is based upon the concept of healing as creation of new ways of *being* a unit of context, that is, for example, a new man, a new society or a new cosmos as represented respectively by a priest, a politician and a humanist biologist fired by an evolutionary vision. Note also how, as we move from East to West on the concepts map, the responsible professional actions embodying the dominant concept of healing involve more and more moral, social, and ultimate choices about the nature and destiny of man.

At this point it must be stressed that the concepts map is deliberately drawn to suggest by implication that there is no one particular concept or cluster of concepts which is the only true one, or universally the best, or which should automatically dominate medical education, medical organization or medical practice. The implication is rather that in the totality of medical practice all concepts should be represented in reasonable proportion by different kinds of healing persons and that individual practitioners and particular health services should give precedence to such concepts as are relevant to the particular situation they face. The idea of an unconditional excellence, an unconditionally best style of being a professional person, unaffected by different times and places, is here under attack. A kind of adaptable catholicity is advocated. Of course any one doctor or medical scientist or health service necessarily operates predominantly with one distribution of concepts on the concepts map, for this is part of human finitude. But this does not reduce the necessity for the practising doctor or medical planner being able to have skill in seeing the problem as if he were elsewhere on the concepts map. If this skill is lacking then communication breaks down and a poor medical service ultimately results. However, while a dominant cluster of concepts is unavoidable for each professional person and for each health care deliverance system it is disastrous if they are the wrong ones for the task in hand. It has been the bane of medicine in the 1920–60s to judge the excellence of every medical identity and every medical unit by concepts in the South-West corner of the concepts map. This corner is where those doctors who work in hospital for the most part operate, and perhaps rightly so, but for them to educate future general practitioners, psychiatrists and medical officers of health to have an identity based on this cluster of concepts is most questionable. For these future doctors and their patients the dominance of the concept of healing as eradication of disease isolated from a unit of context to the exclusion of other concepts of healing is a disaster. This way comes, for example, text books entitled mental *health* which consists solely of descriptions of *diseases* and their eradication. The prominence given to a cluster of concepts must always be relevant to the quite particular task in hand – medical excellence is situational excellence. The task in hand should determine the choice of concepts and not vice versa. So, for example, present-day enthusiastic followers of the psychiatric therapeutic community concept of healing who wish it to dominate hospitals for the acutely ill need to learn adaptable catholicity as do those doctors in acute general hospitals who think the mental health of the community is to be met by acute general hospitals after the fashion of acute appendicitis. If this warning that dominant clusters of concepts of healing are not transferable from one situation to another seems platitudinous let the doubter look around the world. Too often he will find unsuitable ways of health care deliverance being transferred in the twentieth century, just like unsuitable religious practices were in the nineteenth century, to developing countries. A small hospital in a poor country which could not reduce its charges to make its services available to the poorest twenty per cent recently succumbed to the temptation of setting up a cardiac unit as evidence that it was a modern hospital. The result was a rise in all its costs and many more poor were excluded from simple life-saving surgery than benefited from the cardiac unit. The same money and energy diverted to health education might have swung things the other way but the concept of healing as isolation and extraction of disease is very, very seductive and it triumphed. The concepts map helps us to think in adaptable catholicity about such matters, remembering that medical excellence is situational excellence. It is the best response to the needs of people and peoples in particular situations which determine what is first-class medicine and not the faithful copying of the most highly regarded or effective practices of medical schools and teaching hospitals or elsewhere. The little example above shows how a fixed idea of what is first-class medicine can be a hindrance to the health of the people that medicine sets out to serve. It can be a killer.

There is another thing which the concepts map above is intended to demonstrate: the further South-West are the concepts on which a professional person bases his identity the more easy it is for him to operate without anxiety and with recognized success in relative isolation, using the unambiguous criteria of true or untrue, right or wrong, provided by empirical methods. The map tries to demonstrate this by making the squares smaller and more heavily walled to the South-West. Consider the research and practice of microbiology on the one hand and the research and practice of community mental health on the other. It is impossible even to define exactly either community or mental health in a way which will satisfy an empiricist, let alone do a controlled experiment demonstrating unambiguously the value of a method of work on a community, because all variables cannot be controlled. Moreover it is impossible to do community mental health work without involvement in educational policy, political structures, moral choices and ideas – if only provisional – of what a healthy society looks like. The microbiologist may arrive at the truth by straight chain logic, where the truth as it were hangs on the end of a chain of thought and experiment. The community mental health worker arrives at the truth by supporting it with different considerations, and the truth as it were stands like a table on many legs. There is a world of difference between the two decisions—making processes and between the anxieties borne by the two kinds of professionals. The concepts map suggests that medical educators need to produce doctors who are skilled in both kinds of responsible decision-making in such proportions as the needs of the community they serve requires and that they must resist suggesting that one type alone is in some absolute sense the representative of first-class medicine deserving the highest praise, academic honour or financial reward. A first-class medical officer of health will in his lifetime save more lives than most of his colleagues in other work; why is he not equally highly regarded?

There is today a fairly widely held opinion that medical education, organization and practice is still too heavily based on concepts of healing clustered in the South-West corner of the concepts map. The strategy then is to move in a North-East direction. The concepts map suggests that this will involve producing more doctors who:

1. Have skill in appreciating other doctors' concepts of healing.
2. Have an interest and concern for health as well as disease and are trained to operate in the area of value judgments where such an interest in health will take them.

3. Have the skill of making responsible decisions based upon wide ranging information from different disciplines.

4. Have the capacity for resisting the anxiety which comes from not being unambiguously able to demonstrate cure as their idealized teaching hospital mentors can.

5. Have a capacity for caring which is primary and not just secondary to the search for the satisfactions of curing.

6. Are always on the alert and skilled to discover how the changing needs of those for whom they care require a change in their professional self-understanding and in their whole style of being a doctor. This skill in open catholicity may be tomorrow's important virtue in the medical profession.

Finally, it may be pointed out that the concepts map reminds us that any co-operation and dialogue between doctors and theologians can be centred on many different concepts. Of recent years there has been a tendency to suggest that ministers of religion can only co-operate with doctors by becoming knowledgeable and skilled in mental health, by which, unfortunately, is meant not mental health but psychopathology. With this knowledge and skill they can then, it is suggested, become junior partners of doctors in a joint enterprise. The concepts map suggests that this proposed action rather than helping doctors to move from the South-West corner reinforces them in the South-West corner and, to make matters worse, moves the minister of religion from the North-East corner where, in the care of persons in community, in the support of persons in community while they learn through stress, and in inspiration to discover new ways of being man, they have their traditional place. We have already seen the factors required for medicine's move North-East. Could not co-operation with ministers of religion assist? Might it not be that some of the dialogue and co-operation between doctors and ministers of religion might stem from the former learning from the latter competences in the North-East area of concepts of healing as well as vice versa? 'Healthy for what?' and 'Diseased from what?' are both equally important questions and provisional answers to both are always implicit in every medical act. It is time we faced up to this together in joint reflection and joint service. Both medicine and church have too often been guilty of shaping their service according to their established concepts of healing or salvation instead of letting the needs of those they serve question the concepts so dear to their professional identities. (See editor's note on p. 34 below.)

4 Mental Health, Christian Medical Mission and the Future Concept of Comprehensive Health Care

Robert A. Lambourne

Dr Robert A Lambourne was a Lecturer in the Department of Theology in the University of Birmingham.

This chapter is based on a paper given at the annual meeting of the Christian Medical Commission of the World Council of Churches in June 1971.

Dr Lambourne died suddenly on Easter Day 1972 soon after preparing this chapter for publication.

Very little has been done by medical missions for the care of persons suffering from psychotic or neurotic illness compared with their record in other fields of healing. Perhaps more should be done. If so it would make an interesting preparatory research to survey the possible reasons for this situation. Was it a feeling that physical diseases should always have priority? Was it an appreciation that psychiatric care in a foreign culture is especially difficult? Was it a feeling that nothing worthwhile (i.e. cure) could be done with mental illness? Was it some sharp difference between the personality that leads a person into psychiatry and the personality that leads a person into medical mission? Or was it quite other reasons? A careful look at the history of this matter in the last fifty years is surely essential if and when an expansion of medical missionary work in this field is considered. We cannot do this here and now.

A case for such an expansion will not be hard to make. An earlier pre-supposition that 'primitive' societies do not suffer from mental illness has been replaced by a general pre-supposition that psychosis is widespread in all cultures and that unhealthy behaviour of a neurotic kind is equally prevalent in 'primitive' and 'advanced' countries though it may take different forms. The widespread prevalence of alcoholism and other addictions in all cultures and the dramatic rise in suicide and attempted suicide in many fast developing countries is a case in point. In the face of large scale suffering of this kind the case for an expansion of medical mission in this area of sickness does not require lengthy elaboration.

However, before we respond, as I hope we will, to this appeal we should reflect upon the subtler implications of the projects in psychiatry and mental health which we may adopt. Such reflection is necessary, for as we have learned to our cost in the last decade, it is often just the taken-for-granted language and methods of medicine which conceal unrecognized assumptions which have the most far reaching effects. We now recognize that every system of medicine and of medical care has implicit within it a philosophy of personal and political behaviour, and it is not possible to be a missionary for one without being a missionary for the other. This is true when the medicine is concerned with those illnesses called physical. How much more aware then, we must be, of our responsibility when we move as missionaries, whether religious or secular, into the field of psychiatry and mental health in which questions of the nature of true speech and correct social behaviour are so obviously interwoven with the designation of mental illness and its approved treatment. The inevitable *political*[1] ingredient in medical services, previously unrecognized, has become explicit in the last decades as public health has ceased to be only a speciality and become also the originator of a new concept of health. Thus medical mission, always implicitly political, can now be seen to be an explicitly *political* mission. The succeeding argument in this chapter will be that the *personal* philosophy (i.e. suppositions about the nature of a whole or healthy person), inevitably though unconsciously an ingredient in medical services, will become explicit in the next decades as psychiatry ceases to be only a speciality and becomes also the originator of new concepts of health. Medical mission, always implicitly commending one view of the personal, will then be seen to be explicitly *personal* mission.

We will now pursue this analogy between the influence of public health and the influence of psychiatry on the dominant concepts and practices of medicine:

Thirty years ago (Stage 1) public health was a small special subject in the medical curriculum, a speciality among others, and having little influence on the main thinking and practice of medical care.

DIAGRAM 1 A (Compare 2A)

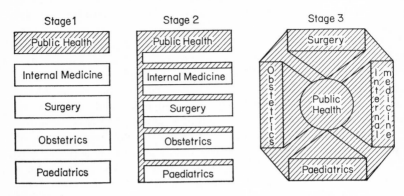

Hatching represents influence of public-health concepts

Public health is a
separate speciality
among speciali-
ties. Unlike 'pure'
medicine it is
undeniably
involved in
politics and
therefore suspect.

Public health
changes some
practices in each
speciality. But
epidemic diseases
remain a special
class of diseases
and each speciality
is judged by
its own results.

Public health changes
the concept of a disease.
Each disease seen now
as an illustration of
epidemiology. Medicine
now seen as comprehen-
sive health care. The
political nature of
medicine is becoming
explicit (see diagrams
below).

Fifteen years ago (Stage 2) public health approaches were to be
found within each speciality but without this changing the specialities' central concepts and practices. Epidemiology still primarily
referred to traditional epidemic diseases of an infectious or con-
tagious nature.

Now (Stage 3) concepts and methods formerly peculiar to public
health have become so central to medicine that they change the
dominant concepts of health and medical care. As a result, for
example, the success of a medical procedure is no longer measured
by the summation of its effect on the same pathology in a number
of individuals. Instead it is measured by considering its effects on
a whole number of factors previously considered to be the interest
solely of other specialities as diverse as agriculture, education,

political philosophy, transportation and industry. This is illustrated in the diagram below:

DIAGRAM 1 B (Compare 2B)

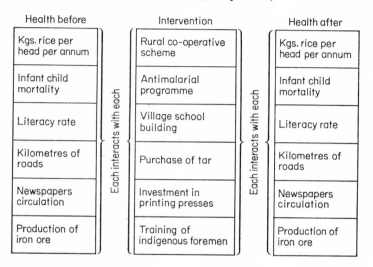

Health before	Intervention	Health after
Kgs. rice per head per annum	Rural co-operative scheme	Kgs. rice per head per annum
Infant child mortality	Antimalarial programme	Infant child mortality
Literacy rate	Village school building	Literacy rate
Kilometres of roads	Purchase of tar	Kilometres of roads
Newspapers circulation	Investment in printing presses	Newspapers circulation
Production of iron ore	Training of indigenous foremen	Production of iron ore

Each interacts with each   Each interacts with each

Notice how the new multivariant method of assessing a good result has as its corollary a new model of health which is constellated and political. As this new model begins to dominate, it begins to make claims for cure based solely upon the measurement of only one factor (e.g. infant mortality), look as self-evidently absurd. It is as if, under the 'traditional' model, adequate success were claimed since all the patients' legs were cured though all the patients died of the same disease! The final stage of this tendency to move from the concept of health as the eradication of all diseases from individuals towards the concept of health as a vital balance of a constellation of factors in acceptable proportions and political harmony is represented by diagram 1C below.

The point being made is that public health has not only made an important impact within its own field but has changed the whole concept of health. It is not just a shift to a preventive view. It is not just that health is no longer seen only as the removal of disease from an individual, and the health of a nation as the summation of such work on such individuals. It is also a shift from an

DIAGRAM 1C (Compare 2C)

Health is objectively indivisible

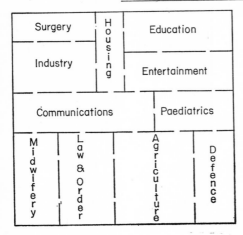

The philosophy of health implicit in the public-health approach has been radicalized within medicine: now a 'health' report is inseparable from part of a 'state of the nation' report, and vice-versa.

The concept of HEALTH and the concept of JUSTICE are now inextricably entangled

individual to a corporate multivariant view of health so that now a nation's health report can clearly be seen as part of a report on the whole political-economic state of the nation. This change can be indicated by saying that public-health concepts of medicine have been radicalized to the point at which 'health' and 'justice', while remaining different notions, can no longer be considered as separable notions. One indication of this is that medicine has become politicalized to the point at which (see diagram above) political maturity is seen not only as a *means* of health but as one *measure* of health!

Let us now develop the analogy between the recent influence of public health on medicine on the one hand and the possible future influence of psychiatry and mental health care on medicine on the other hand. The diagrams which follow illustrate the comparable stages.

From the diagrams we can see that while psychiatry can exist as a separate discipline concerned to care for individuals with psychiatric illness it can also, like public health, begin first to influence the approach to all types of diseases as traditionally understood, and eventually become a unifying concept which changes the

DIAGRAM 2 A (Compare 1A)

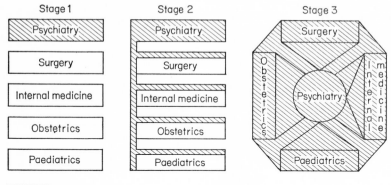

Hatching represents influence of psychiatric concepts

Healing is the personal management of individual diseases. Psychiatry is a separate speciality. Psychodynamics is knowledge about individual psychosis or neurosis only.

Now there is Psychological awareness in personal management of all individual diseases. Psychiatry is beginning to affect the concept of health but psychodynamics is still only to do with psychosis or neurosis.

Each single disease is seen now as an example of a disturbance in an interpersonal psychological situation. Psychiatry is now changing the concept of health, of how it is pursued, and by what criteria it is measured.

understanding of what health is and by what criteria it is to be measured. Finally, just as the radicalization of the public health approach to medicine produced a situation where 'health' and 'justice' can no longer be considered as entirely separable notions, so the radicalization of the psychiatric approach to medicine produces a situation where 'health' and 'persons in harmonious living' (love) can no longer be considered as entirely separate notions. As public health can revolutionize medicine by changing the concept of health so that it becomes close to the idea of a political utopia, so psychiatry can revolutionize medicine by changing the concept of health so that it becomes close to the idea of a community in a state of ideal personal wholeness and well being. The result of this will be to introduce a new range of multivariants into the measurement of interventions in disease situations as they are increasingly introduced in the developing practice of comprehensive health care. However, in this case these multivariants will not be socio-economic but will be concerned with what are considered to be desirable personal and interpersonal qualities. (Probably these will tend to be denoted in recognizably psychological terminology and supposedly legitimated by psychological science whereas in the past centuries they were denoted in recognizably ethical terminology and supposedly legitimated by theology. Comprehensive mental health care practices will inevitably disseminate views about what is the best way of living our lives. These views will be highly conditioned by the brand of humanism congenial to the professionals who develop them.) This means that diagrams to illustrate programmes of proposed medical action and the criteria to measure the resultant effects may look like this:

DIAGRAM 2 B (Compare 1B)

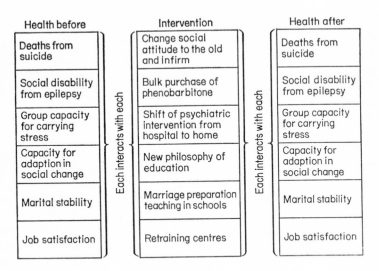

Health before	Intervention	Health after
Deaths from suicide	Change social attitude to the old and infirm	Deaths from suicide
Social disability from epilepsy	Bulk purchase of phenobarbitone	Social disability from epilepsy
Group capacity for carrying stress	Shift of psychiatric intervention from hospital to home	Group capacity for carrying stress
Capacity for adaption in social change	New philosophy of education	Capacity for adaption in social change
Marital stability	Marriage preparation teaching in schools	Marital stability
Job satisfaction	Retraining centres	Job satisfaction

(Each interacts with each)

And it means that the introduction of psychiatric concepts into medicine has become radicalized to produce a new concept of health in which the nation of 'health' and the notion of 'an ideal state of souls in fellowship' are no longer entirely separable.

DIAGRAM 2C (Compare 1C)

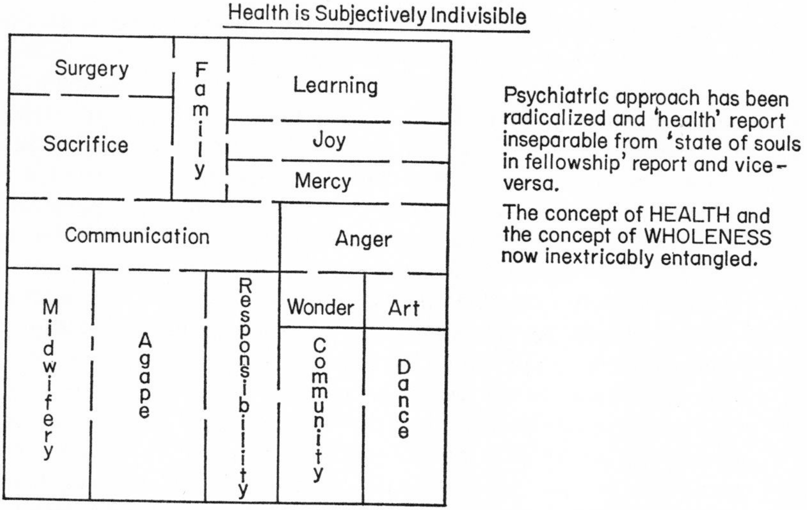

Health is Subjectively Indivisible

Surgery	F a m i l y	Learning	
Sacrifice		Joy	
		Mercy	
Communication		Anger	

(Diagram continued — lower portion)

M i d w i f e r y		A g a p e		R e s p o n s i b i l i t y	Wonder	Art
					C o m m u n i t y	D a n c e

Psychiatric approach has been radicalized and 'health' report inseparable from 'state of souls in fellowship' report and vice-versa.

The concept of HEALTH and the concept of WHOLENESS now inextricably entangled.

The end result of this impact of the public-health concept on medicine is to bring the philosophy of medicine closer to the philosophy of 'politics' largely conceived of as a technological task. The resultant style of comprehensive health care will tend to be numerate, managerial and power conscious, in which health will be conceived of as one among many material possessions to which every human being has a right.

The end result of the impact of the 'psychiatric' concept of medicine is to bring the philosophy of medicine close to the philosophy of 'love' largely conceived of as a personal task of interpersonal relations. The resultant style will be literate, obedient, imaginative and humble in which health will be conceived of as a surprising joy to which every human being comes by grace.

We see then how within the changing processes of secular medicine and its technological shifts are invitations to us to perennially transcend our previous understandings of health and of the health-care system which brings mankind closer to health. If public-health concepts imply a 'political' revolution in medicine, psychiatric concepts imply an 'experiential' revolution in medicine. We have already seen how political community participation may be advocated not merely as a means to community health but as

one criterion of community health. Similarly the manner in which
men and women experience their own and others' illnesses, healing, and health may become an inseparable part of the definition
and measurement of illness, healing and health. What does this
mean for the future of medical mission?

As we become increasingly conscious that men and women can
choose the criteria by which to measure the health towards which
they can be assisted by health care the challenge to medical
mission becomes more evident. They are challenged first to discern
with those they serve what health might mean for them and
secondly to act with those they serve to bring that health nearer.
For health is God's continual activity and medical mission is
called to be fellow-workers in that activity.

What should be the challenge to comprehensive health-care
practices of an experiential philosophy of health supported by
psychiatric and mental-health approaches to healing? The challenge to these comprehensive health-care services as they become
generalized in the next twenty years should not be a call for a
return to the old individualistic approach which neglected the
many for the care of the few. It should rather take the form of a
new emphasis on the personal and interpersonal experiences of
human beings when they are confronted with disease in themselves or in others. It should protest that the quantitative methods
necessarily employed in comprehensive health care grossly under-
weigh in their human accountancy those personal subjective factors
which are highly prized when the definition of health properly
includes an optimal personal response of men and women to their
own or their neighbour's disease. It should complain whenever the
objectives of a comprehensive approach to health become in-
sufficiently comprehensive because statistical methods tend to
exclude subjective elements of personal response and freedom in
their estimation of what is worthwhile expenditure of scarce medical resources. It should point to the way in which thereby a new
class of poor persons deprived of their needs for health care
are created. These new poor are those persons whose medical
care is estimated to be unwarranted because disease eradication,
which by medicine is so often *implicitly* assumed to be the self-
evident goal of health care, through a strict accountancy approach
becomes *explicitly* the goal of health care. This comes about
through the well-known tendency of the methods of planning and
decision-making to shape the definition of the task in hand. The

end result in this case might be that the care of the incurable might be regarded as an affront to justice!

An example of the new poor might be the chronic schizophrenic. Not only does his treatment involve none of that scientific technology which is so prestigious in modern medicine but since he is irrational, unproductive and seemingly incurable a comprehensive health care based upon an objective distribution of scarce resources does not merely seem to allow his neglect but almost to demand it! Only if our concept of health includes as an important criterion of its measurement a growing capacity of persons to constitute a hopeful, helpful and sacrificial fellowship in the face of unbearable and unprofitable situations is such an approach explicitly irrational. Without such a concept of health a comprehensive health care system, priding itself on its objectivity, could come to obscure a large area of responsibility for health care analagous to the way in which in the immediate past a type of hospital care which was too turned in on itself obscured the responsibility to care for those sick who did not present themselves at hospital.

Psychiatry and mental health might then open up new ways of understanding comprehensive health care, ways which provide a counter balance to the concepts and practices of health which tend to follow when most priority is given by comprehensive health care to measures which, at low cost, cure or prevent physical illness. But this corrective is not to be taken for granted. Also possible is a type of psychiatry and mental health which actually reinforces the tendency of comprehensive care to make healing a managerial, industrial activity. Which of these possibilities should be the main aim for medical mission? This must depend in part on a theological decision as to which vital parts of a true understanding of man's wholeness are in danger of being overlooked in current health care.

It seems, then, that if, as I believe we should, we seriously consider the possibility that psychiatry and mental health have an increasing part to play in Christian medical mission in the years to come we should take a long careful look at what we propose to do. We now realize that the deliverance of physical health care necessarily involves a particular 'political' way of life and that one cannot escape altogether from 'political' commitment in medical mission for physical health care. What we have demonstrated above is that psychiatric services and mental-health care necessarily involve a particular 'personal' way of life and that one cannot escape altogether from 'personal' commitment in the consequent comprehensive health care. The use of anthropologists, sociologists and educationalists to master the ways of life of poorer peoples in order to innovate programmes for improving their physical health needs to be done with great sensitivity if it is not to be an affront to human freedom and dignity. Even more sensitivity and patience is required in a psychiatric or mental-health programme. Otherwise there will evolve a kind of mental-health evangelism which will properly earn the accusation of being disguised imperialism. Nevertheless, if the thesis of this chapter is correct there cannot be a complete separation of the vigorous pursuit of a mental health programme from the commendation of a particular personal philosophy of life. Healing and salvation thus occur together in secular forms as the intertwining of health care with an assumption, even if it be a tentative assumption, about the nature of wholeness. Thus in secular form there rises again the question of the relation between preaching and humanist service. There is no way out of this dilemma by opting for a so called scientific medicine free of personal and political values. This is not a live option. The question of the relation between proclamation and humanist service is thus inescapable.

NOTE

1. I am aware that the word 'political' may be offensive to many but I know of no substitute word to indicate the network of management, organizations, sanctions, etc., which are found in every society and without which social human life and a medical service would be impossible.

Editor's note: The diagram of Dr Lambourne's 'concept map' on p.18 above shows remarkable similarities to a diagram entitled 'Human Perspectives' which appears on p.19 of a book entitled *The Limits to Growth. A Report for the Club of Rome's Project on the Predicament of Mankind*, by D. H. Meadows and others, 1972 (Earth Island Ltd, London).

5 The Ethics of Social Work: Some Questions and Affirmations

Marjorie Inkster

After six years' technical work on radar, Marjorie Inkster took an English Honours Degree in London, followed by two years post-graduate theology in Cambridge. Then came five years as Chaplains' Assistant, Royal Air Force, the Mental Health Course at London School of Economics, and two years as Assistant Minister at the City Temple. A career in psychiatric social work ended as Head Psychiatric Worker at St Bartholomew's Hospital.

For the last two and a half years she has been in social work training and development in Hackney and Harrow.

In 1961, she delivered ten lectures on The Ethics of Social Work at the North-Western Polytechnic, much helped by the *Sociological Review, Monograph* No. 3 (Keele University 1960), which is the report of the Keele Conference of the same year on 'Moral Issues and the Training of Teachers and Social Workers'. This present article, founded on her lectures, incorporates some of her more recent thinking on the subject.

An attempt to define

The study of economic theory can be said to be 'scientific' because it deals with man as he *is*. When the economist attempts predictions he tries to state what men *will* do, rather than what they *ought* to do. In the field of ethics, however, we are not so much concerned with the actual characteristics of men's behaviour as with the ideals. Why, then, should social workers and others concerned with the social sciences have their time wasted with something which is completely unscientific?

A re-reading of the work of many of the philosophers might make us ask that question again. Hume drew a sharp distinction between 'ought' and 'is'. Kant did the same. He called for a sort of 'division of labour' in thought about man, in which he strictly separated ethics (which he said should be a pure *a priori* science) from what he called 'anthropology', by which he meant what we now call the social sciences. The latter, he said, should be empirical – a sort of condensation of what man was actually found to be (like the economic man). Professor Nowell-Smith, speaking on 'Ethics and Psychology',[1] comments that it is generally said that the job of social scientists is 'to describe and explain human behaviour and motives as they actually are, not to give good or bad marks or to tell us what human behaviour ought to be'. When we talk of a science, then, we simply mean a specialized form of knowledge. And surely any science worthy of the name includes not only what is, but what might be; if it does not it can never advance. As D. V. Donnison has said: 'Social reform is a product, not merely of knowledge, but of inventive thought and moral judgment.'[2] To a certain extent inventive thought is dependent upon moral judgment, because unless you think that things *ought* to be different, you are unlikely to search for ways to make them so.

Freud, speaking as an analyst, once said: 'We are observers, not reformers.' Social workers are trained to absorb into their own disciplined way of work one of the basic principles of therapy – that of complete acceptance of the client. But in the very concept of therapy itself – and this includes analysis and social work – lies the idea that this particular patient, this particular client, this mother, this father, this family, this child, *ought* not to be in this state – of depression, or agitation, or inability to show affection. Everyone who undertakes any kind of work which involves healing or helping people must feel that the person who is in a 'therapeutic relationship' *ought* to be able to cope with life *better*. If a mother has given up all attempt to keep her children clean, her home ordered and her husband happy and we feel that such a family is just as 'good' as one in which the mother is able to do all these things – then what on earth are we doing in the health or social services at all?

Classical ethics has a great deal to say about a *summum bonum*, which is said to be happiness. Therapists tend to trot out clichés about self-discovery being painful but worthwhile. *How* painful does it have to be before it is no longer worthwhile to the patient? What do we mean when we say that a client in a casework situation is 'better' or 'worse'? Do we mean happier, less dependent, or more mature? What do we mean by 'mature'? If, for instance, a therapist, as a complete agnostic, found that his client was inclining towards a religious belief, would he label him as an obsessional?

Would he consider that this new development was an indication of the need for further therapy? How do we each decide when we think another human being is mature?

If we who call ourselves social scientists are concerned that things should be 'better' than they are, then we need an ethic, whether it be a personal one, or one which we can hold in common with other social workers. If we feel that the aim of casework or group work is to help people towards a greater maturity, we must ourselves have some conception of what maturity is. But at the same time, if we have any sense of the value of a person and respect for that person as a person, we shall not seek to mould him or her into a preconceived pattern of what we think he should be. This is something of a dilemma and I shall look at the problem more fully later. There is no doubt that we must take heed of Lady Wootton's warning against the arrogance of social workers who are too ready to manage other people's lives. If this is true of us – and I think each of us must examine his own work continually in the light of this criticism – then the main motive in choosing this work has been not the needs of other people but our own. We need to examine our motivation also in greater detail.

There has been implicit in much social work training the assumption that one must always look behind the simple request for help and explore the deeper motives and needs which lie behind. Lady Wootton has something very scathing to say about this also. She issues a sharp warning against the view that 'those who are invited to deal with one matter are entitled also to explore others, or that it is proper to give professional training in the art of extracting from those who seek help on one problem details of others of a more intimate personal nature.'[3] Elizabeth Howarth has written: 'Students may become so dazzled by the complexities of casework that they can miss the wonderfully helpful and simple things which can be done. They lose sight of the rule that the caseworker is only called upon to do as much as is necessary to the immediate situation.'[4] There is a real temptation to use one's skill to explore further than the problem demands, and the answer lies in what we mean by respect for the person.

If we envisage some sort of maturity for ourselves and for our clients, how do we envisage a maturity for our whole social structure? Need we do so? Ought we to do so? Might we not, as social workers, retreat into some snug little corner of our own, where we get the opportunity to do some 'intensive casework' and perhaps quite often see gratifying results, or find another sort of retreat in the hectic routine of administrative work in some local authority? Or should we try to retain an awareness of what is going on around us, of social trends, or possibilities of change, of *prevention* of things which at the moment we are struggling to mend? Perhaps, while concentrating on our own particular job as we see it needs to be done, we can remain aware that administrators need information and co-operation from us so that laws may eventually be made which will alter the basic structure. We might look beyond the small waves made by our own individual struggles, out on to the sea of statistics which represents other people's casework and administrative work. We might try to retain a perspective of the ocean.

There may be – indeed there will be – ways in which what we think we ought to do in a certain situation conflicts with what the law tells us we may do. There will almost certainly be many times when what we think we ought to do will conflict with what our colleagues think we ought to do, or what people from other agencies think we ought to do. There will be times when our loyalties to our client will conflict with our loyalties to our agency. There will be times when we think that a colleague ought not to have done this or that – and when the particular 'this or that' which was done definitely prevents us from doing what we think we ought to have done. We have to learn to work within the limitations of the law or the regulations of our particular agency; sometimes not just within the limitations of what we judge to be right, but within the narrower ones of what is possible. The results of new legislation and of social security are not always what we think they should be. Continually we are in situations where we have to balance one good against another, or, what is even more difficult, one half-good against another, one compromise against another.

They say that to understand all is to forgive all. Is this true? Are social workers never to feel a sort of moral indignation against clients who react to what society does for them with greed or apathy? And what about our moral indignation against a society which appears blind to social evils which we have encountered at first-hand? To understand as much as we can seems to be part of our aim. But even if it were possible to know every detail of our client's life and of his parents' lives and grandparents' lives, would we yet understand completely why *he* reacted to his tyrannical father with aggression, while his brother did not? Is it entirely a matter of where he stands in order of birth in the family? There is the story of the small boy who went home with a rather fearsome school report. He gave it to his father and after a long and ominous pause, during which the latter digested it, he said perkily: 'What do you think is the matter with me, Dad – heredity or environment?' Well, these two things, heredity and environment are two of the things which are the matter with all of us. We have all had parents and grandparents and great-grandparents. We all have had to be born and brought up somewhere by somebody. But is this all? Freud's thinking, like all great human thought, has much in it that is paradoxical. A great deal of it is deterministic. We are perhaps ambivalent about this. But how far is our contention that we should not judge others based on belief that they are not, in fact, free agents, but are the slaves of their unconscious motivation? Are we to abolish law courts altogether and introduce instead a series of graded psychiatric clinics? Do we believe that an individual has any real responsibility for his own actions?

I mentioned earlier two of the main tenets of casework theory – acceptance of a client and helping him towards greater maturity (always supposing that we have some ideas as to what maturity is). We could list several other principles of casework. It might be worthwhile to look back towards the sources of these. We often speak so glibly about them, without examining or questioning the origins of either principles or techniques. They go further back than Gordon Hamilton![5] Are the techniques in themselves sufficient to heal, to repair damaged lives and enable men's and women's minds and emotions to mature? Or does it matter what kind of men and women the social workers are? I shall explore some of these sources and also attempt some sort of exploration into the kind of love needed in casework.

The final question concerns again the principles of casework. Are these principles variable and will they change with the fashions of the times? Are they part of some inevitable evolutionary process, or some dialectic? Do human beings possess within themselves all the potentialities needed to ensure progress? Why does this so-called 'progress' matter? Is this all part of an instinctive move towards preservation of the race? As we look at the evolution of thought in regard to social casework, group work and community work, should we not also keep on the perimeter of our vision the ideas of Nietzsche and the survival of the fittest? Why do we protect the weak, and is it good always to do so? Why does it matter whether we try to prevent children from being ill-treated or not? Why does it matter whether we mind or not? There is indeed no end to such questions. There would be something seriously wrong if we did not ask them continually. The important thing is not to be able to answer them all, but to be aware of the need to question.

Motivation in choosing to take up social work. The need for self-knowledge

Imagine a group of students on a social-work course. Why are they there at all? If they were asked, would they say it was primarily because they wanted to be? I do not mean that they want to be at that particular seminar, but that they want to work with deprived children, with handicapped people, with families with problems. Or would they put it more accurately by saying that they feel they ought to work with these people who need help? Can they equate the 'want' and the 'ought' the whole time?

Almost certainly most would say: 'I don't particularly want to have to work long hours and irregular ones. I don't want to have to study again and submit myself to the criticism of tutors. But I cannot help seeing a need.' Perhaps they would add that having read about, and often having seen for themselves, these human problems, knowing that there are not enough trained social workers to cope with half, their consciences would not allow them *not* to undertake the work. Are they then undertaking this work to assuage their own consciences – because otherwise they would not be able to 'sleep o' nights'? Or do social workers know themselves as people who need to be needed? Are we all seeking first our own happiness – or that of other people – or do we believe these two go together?

The American Declaration of Independence speaks of the 'rights' of the individual and 'rights' here include 'the pursuit of happiness'. But there are a good many thinkers today who say that men do not actually seek happiness. Happiness is the result of achieving some desired end, of satisfying a need. Several modern thinkers, especially the existentialists, would query the whole concept of the pleasure-pain principle. In *Love, Power and Justice*, Tillich says:

Man strives to reunite himself with that to which he belongs and from which he is separated ... All living beings desire food, movement, growth, participation in a group, sexual union, etc. The fulfilment of these desires is accompanied by pleasure. But it is not the pleasure as such which is desired but the union with that which fulfils the desire. Fulfilled desire is pleasure and un-fulfilled desire is pain. But it is a distortion of the actual pro-cesses of life to deduce from this that life essentially consists of fleeing from pain and striving for pleasure. Wherever this hap-pens life is corrupted. Unperverted life strives for that of which it is in want; it strives for union with that which is separated from it.[6]

Everyone in the helping professions has to face up to the fact that he or she is a person who needs to cure, to put right, to mend. Watch a small child with her doll. She is angry with it and bashes it hard against the side of her chair, holding it by the hair. Or perhaps her big brother seizes it and heaves it across the room. It is a rag doll and is not damaged. Yet the child pretends it is injured. She bandages it. She gives it medicine. She holds it in her arms and comforts it. Then she puts it to bed and tucks it up safely. In five minutes the doll is well again. She has cured it by her nursing. She can cure any of her dolls. Some of the big American toy-manufacturers must be the worst psychologists on earth. Just before Christmas, a few years ago, dolls were being sold in a New York store with ready-made injuries – manufactured with damaged limbs, bodies or faces. They did not leave the injuries to the child's imagination: but neither – and this is the important part – did they allow for that miraculous cure, that magical nursing back to health, which gives a child such pleasure.

It is important for us to acknowledge the greater or lesser ex-tent of this desire for therapeutic power in ourselves for it is part of the desire for omnipotence. Adler regarded the will-to-power as the basic impulse in us. Karen Horney discussed at length in *The Neurotic Personality of our Time*[7] how she saw the will-to-power and the libidinous impulses described by Freud as derivatives of anxiety. The existentialist theologian would say that the anxiety which causes much of the tension to be found in the least neurotic of men is due to the fact that we are finite and imperfect beings. Part of our growing-up, our maturing, is in learning and accepting that we are not magicians, we are not omnipotent. There are many sicknesses and immaturities, many broken homes, which we can never cure, never put right. We have to learn these unpleasant

truths in our own private lives and in our relationships with
friends. But in social work, whether it be with the mentally ill or
the socially deprived, we are continually confronted with situations
in which we have to acknowledge ourselves wholly or partially
impotent. The chronic schizophrenic, the alcoholic, the emergent
delinquent, the apparently irresponsible young unmarried mother
with eight children, together with many others, challenge our
desire to put things right, or to enable them to put things right!

During their training period, it is essential that embryo social
caseworkers and other social workers come to terms with their
own reactions to intractable problems. Is it necessary for a social
worker to develop a thick skin and adopt a cynical attitude? If
not, what must he do with his guilt because he cannot mend this
or that broken family? Perhaps he has the job of taking Mary, aged
four, and Jackie, aged two, into care for the third time. If he feels
guilt, can he relate this in any way to his choice of child care work
in the first place? Is he there, in that filthy backyard or that smart
council flat, primarily to assuage his own guilt that such situations
exist – or is he there to help a child in the only way he can be
helped at the moment? Or is it a mixture of both? Thomas à
Kempis, one of the great medieval scholars, said: 'Many secretly
seek themselves in what they do and know it not.'

If our work cannot be entirely selfless – and I think we must
agree that this is so – how can we minimize in ourselves the anger
and irritation and retaliative desires which wait upon what many
outsiders call our 'failures'? Is it right to think we have failed,
where we could not 'succeed'? I have known even a trained therapist lash out at a patient, refusing to treat him further, rejecting
him because he has not used the treatment as the therapist thought
he should: this, even where the therapist knew that this was the
pattern which the patient had encouraged over and over again in
life … a pattern which above all things should be broken. This is
so often exactly what has happened to many of the so-called
'problem families'. If there is little we can do effectively to help
them, can we not at least retain our original concern for them?
It is our guilt about our own ineffectiveness which makes us turn
on them or reject them. They are a challenge to our desire for
omnipotence, our wish to make all things good. Sometimes a
caseworker's failure lies in having refused to face up to failure!

So much of a social worker's effectiveness depends upon his or
her own emotional maturity. He may have gained some of the

essential insights into his own make-up during training, but it is difficult for him to develop these, to discover new ones and to continue to 'grow', if he works too much in isolation from colleagues, or, if working from the same office, does not learn to share his experiences and discoveries with them. Margaret Ferard, in *Boundaries of Casework*,[8] speaks of the difficulties of developing beyond the point which one reached at the end of training, if there is no 'team' of trained people with whom one can discuss. The continual reappraisal and reassessment of what one is doing is almost impossible when one has only one's own perspective from which to work. When thrown almost entirely upon one's own resources, casework easily becomes sterile. It is such a valuable experience to see one's cases through other people's eyes. Even when a worker has been through a formal analysis, it is fatally easy to indulge in self-justification. A Sunday-school teacher was telling the children about the Pharisees and the publican. She said unctuously: 'The Pharisee prayed: "Lord, I thank thee that I am not as other men are", and the publican said: "Lord, be merciful to me, a sinner" ...and now, boys and girls, we should thank God we are not like the Pharisee.'

We see that there is a real need for each of us to make continual judgments, which are in fact moral judgments, upon ourselves, in our work. Here we come to the Christian doctrine of sin. Nothing could be more relevant. For first, although it teaches that we need continually to take a long, hard look at ourselves and our motivation, it contains also the essential optimism. It looks at us all, with our misdirected aggression, our hypocrisies, our jealousies and our insecurities, and says: 'We are not meant to be like this ... we are not meant to be like that.' This is the essentially ethical statement. We ought not to be like this. We ought to know ourselves better. We ought not to deceive ourselves. We ought not to project our own feelings of rejection on to other people and so grow resentful of imagined insults ... and so on. But the second, equally important, point about this Christian doctrine is that it accepts and asks us to accept that we are imperfect and will continue to be so. It should therefore give us two things. First a tension between 'is' and 'ought' – a tension necessary to all human action. Secondly, if truly accepted, a means of avoiding the extremes of pathological guilt, or desire for omnipotence, which can corrupt motive and action.

Dr Laycock in an article on 'Ethics and Social Work' says:

'It is a professional obligation on the social worker to meet the client's needs primarily, not his own – and this demands a capacity both for self-awareness and self-discipline.'[9] We have looked at some of the aspects of self-awareness. But how are we to achieve the self-discipline? Therapists and case-workers who have been analysed – and have presumably achieved a degree of self-aware-ness – but have not yet found the way to self-discipline, are all too common. What is self-discipline? Freud would have us believe that knowledge brings control, rather in the same way as the Greeks believed that knowledge eliminated what Christians call sin. But does it not depend a lot on what we feel we ought to control and why? Here we are again up against an ethical question. If, for instance, we were to learn all there was to know about our own particular sexual urges, that knowledge would not prevent us from using them in a way which might be destructive to another person or damaging to society. Jesus promised that a man in losing him-self would 'find' himself. Some people therefore go all out for martyrdom. But the martyr-like helper of others often does not look much like a fulfilled person – a person who has 'found him-self'. Other people live and work in a way which they think should bring them most satisfaction. This may include making or keep-ing someone else dependent upon them. One would suspect that a few casework supervisors have chosen to do the work for this reason. Have they in so doing found 'fullness' of life?

If we examine our own motives for working as we do, we find that there are many situations in which what we feel we ought to do is not at all what we would like to do. If our *summum bonum* is happiness, we have to account for the fact that our sense of 'oughtness' often conflicts with our desires. Can we explain this simply in terms of masochistic impulses – that causing ourselves pain or discomfort in itself brings a sort of happiness? The more one thinks of it, the more it becomes obvious that one simply can-not explain in this way all situations in which 'oughtness' conflicts with our own personal desires. For instance, a group of social workers may be agreed that one course of action is right. Yet in that group the action decided upon may give satisfaction to some and cause anxiety and emotional disturbance in others. One can-not explain a group decision of this kind simply by saying that some of its members are masochists and some are not! There must be some criteria other than their individual reactions of pain or pleasure, on which the decision is based.

If we say, with Tillich, that our main aim in life is 'striving for that of which we are in want', 'striving for union with that from which we are separated', we are saying that our actions tend towards a goal of drive-reduction – a state of quiescence. This might suggest that the ideal, the *summum bonum*, was a sort of Buddhist Nirvana, in which all striving, all desire has gone. Yet most of us who have been brought up in a Western civilization feel that it would be terrible not to have anything left for which to strive. The old proverb, 'It is better to travel hopefully than to arrive', speaks not so much of possible disillusion at the end of every journey, as of the joy and satisfaction in the action, in the travelling.

In this travelling, in this action, there is a continual element of choice. There is the age-old challenge of the book of Deuteronomy: 'I have set before you life and good, death and evil ... therefore choose life' (Deut. 30.19). The continual need to choose, the moving in a certain direction, towards, presumably, what we think of as a fuller life, cannot be unaccompanied by tension. In electronics, it is known that current cannot flow unless there is a difference between the voltage of one terminal and another. This difference, interestingly enough, is called a 'potential'. It seems that human psychological make-up is such that a person cannot summon up enough energy for action unless he not only recognizes the 'better' and 'worse' elements in a situation, but sees himself as in some way involved in it, or 'switched-on'. Of course he may choose a course of action which is only better for him. He may choose one which is better for society or for some other individual. He may choose one which is a mixture of both. Depending on his insight into his own motivation, his own maturity or immaturity, he will be more or less conscious of why he is choosing this course.

Psychiatrists and social caseworkers tend to contrast maturity and neuroticism in a rather glib way. In many people whom we would label 'neurotic' there is a great deal of tension between themselves and the outside (or 'real'?) world. The neurotic, being in conflict with reality and only able to live with a *part* of his being, is a restricted self. But sometimes, by the very nature of his neurosis, he makes up for this by the intensity of his living. While the average person is fighting on a broader front and therefore feels less tension, the neurotic, confronted with greater tension, may respond by becoming a creative artist – or perhaps a reformer. Many psychiatrists would label Florence Nightingale as 'neurotic', saying that she was escaping from her own sexuality. They would say that Lord Shaftesbury was trying to alleviate his own guilt, because he had been born a wealthy aristocrat. But does this completely explain Florence Nightingale or Lord Shaftesbury? D. V. Donnison speaks thus of social reform.

The social reformer must be prepared to assert a preference – to say: This is the kind of world I want to live in. Psychologically (rather than logically) speaking, the capacity to stick one's neck out in this way is generally derived from a capacity for being shocked about the human condition – from sympathy with the unfortunate or a sense of outrage at the sight of social injustice. It is this feeling for people that forces us to question accepted ways of doing things and to look beyond the confines of any one professional or administrative sphere. Can it be taught? I suspect it has more to do with the way in which different academic subjects are linked up and applied to the study of society than with the particular selection of subjects chosen.[10]

Charlotte Towle contends that an essential preparation for work in one of the professions is education concerned to develop the good parent, good neighbour and good citizen.[11] If this is so, the kind of self-knowledge which the professional social worker needs to develop may come best through learning in the three dimensions of individual one-to-one casework, group work and community work. It is sometimes very difficult to know how to be a good parent *and* a good citizen. Perhaps the fact that we cannot always be both links up with what was said earlier about coming to terms with our own desire for omnipotence.

An attempt to seek the origins of principles broadly subscribed to by social workers

In the general study of ethics, there appear to be three key words, empiricism, rationalism and intuitionism. The empiricists see our principles of right and wrong as having developed from the actual experiences of mankind – a crystallization of the discoveries man has made in his attempts to adapt to his environment, a sort of case-law of life. The rationalists see reason as the means by which we may know what is right and what is wrong – more or less independently of experience. To the Greeks, knowledge was akin to virtue. To know all things would be to act rightly. Hence the difficulties they had in accepting the Christian interpretation of Jesus' crucifixion, because it was completely beyond all reason. The Greeks would not have found it easy to say as the Hebrew psalmist did: 'Such knowledge is too wonderful for me. It is high. I cannot attain unto it' (Ps. 139.6). The Jews were better than the Greeks at coming to terms with the fact that they were not and never could be omniscient. The intuitionists say that man has an instinctive grasp of moral values as such. Like a sort of sixth sense, the 'moral sense', if developed sufficiently, would find the right answer to all problems of thought and action. Kant's categorical imperative says to us: 'Act only on that principle which thou canst at the same time *will* to become universal law.' The essence of evil consists in treating one's own case as exceptional.

There is a great deal of truth in the empiricists' theories. There is a case-law of life. Margaret Mead and other modern anthropologists have shown us that many principles which we might be tempted to regard as 'basic' principles apply only to our particular part of the world or way of life. Tribal codes and religious teachings concerning such things as sexual relations inside and outside of marriage vary to an extraordinary degree. Some communities seem to survive with a high degree of 'promiscuity' generally accepted by all. In others, sexual intercourse outside marriage is punishable by death. In others again, it is considered that a 'trial period' should be the norm. Codes and conventions dealing with treatment of relatives, property-holding, hospitality, common responsibilities and so on vary to an amazing extent in different parts of the world. Incest, although widely accepted as 'not good', is not regarded as intrinsically evil throughout the world. We explain incest taboos by saying that too much close in-breeding leads to the deterioration of the species. But if this is so, what have the empiricists to say about the parts of the world where incest is allowed? Why have men in these areas not deduced from their experience of life the moral concept that incest is wrong? Christians have imposed their ideas concerning monogamy upon people with very different family structures. But it is important to be continually aware that what is good and right for one community is not necessarily best for another. We might note in passing that Freud's Oedipal theory, resting as it does upon a close father-mother-child relationship, may have little or no meaning in communities where such a family pattern does not exist. Different family experiences in childhood may affect development of the super-ego.

Rationalistic theories also contain a good deal of truth. Not knowing about the suffering of people prevents us from going to their aid. Lack of knowledge of the correct medical care can lead us to cause greater suffering, for instance, putting the wrong substance on a burn. Lack of knowledge of the principles of therapy can lead us to total failure in efforts to help a neurotic or immature person. Lack of self-knowledge can distort our understanding of other people. Good intention, good feeling, by itself is never sufficient.

Finally, if we look again at the theories of the intuitionists, who insist that we apprehend a universal law by some inborn moral sense, we see much with which a religious man would agree. Many agnostic or atheistic thinkers are aware of, and ready to acknowledge, a widespread need in men to believe in some God, some Presence, some Law and Spirit which transcends all human experience and reason. Rupert Brooke parodies this most delightfully in his poem 'Heaven':

> Fish say, they have their Stream and Pond:
> But is there anything Beyond?

The fish picture their God:

> Immense, of fishy form and mind;
> Squamous, omnipotent and kind;
> And under that Almighty Fin,
> The littlest fish may enter in.

They speculate.

> One may not doubt that, somehow, Good
> Shall come of Water and of Mud;
> And sure the reverent eye must see
> A Purpose in Liquidity.

Some say that this kind of thinking is due to our reluctance to believe that we stand alone, a refusal to give up the infantile beliefs and wishes about parental figures which we held in babyhood. Some say that we men and women cannot bear the weight of our own moral responsibility – responsibility for ourselves and others; that we cannot endure the thought of the loneliness and meaninglessness of human life lived without a God: so we invent one. But the 'Honest to God' and 'God is dead' approach to theology seems very naïve to anyone whose studies are grounded

in the work of the great twentieth-century theologians; because it
largely ignores the fact that God is not an object – he is the Subject, the 'Great I AM', the Beginning. The best Christian theology
has always taught that God is both immanent and transcendent.
Even if we would, we could not 'kill him off', as the infant often
wants to kill a parent – and believes he can do so. God IS, in spite
of the mess we make of our own lives and of the lives of others.

Compare the Greek and Hebrew attitudes to these things for a
moment. To Plato, Aristotle and other Greek thinkers, ethics and
politics are inseparable. If the highest good can be realized only
in a community, the state is the organ of morality. Plato says as
much in the *Republic*. If we are to believe the Greeks, a naturalistic moral philosophy, one deduced from facts known, is possible. Possessing reason and being confronted with certain basic
facts of human existence, we can deduce moral judgments from
them. And from these we can build a framework of laws and
principles of life on which we can base all action and thought.

The Hebrews started the other way round. To them it seemed
that God, the initiator, the wholeness of truth and love, confronted
human reason, knowledge and emotion with his word, his law and
his love. Man could never have attained to knowledge of his law
except by the divine initiative. The psalmist who wrote Ps. 139
experienced things this way and so did the prophets. The Jews felt
that the Ten Commandments, many of which appear in varied
form in earlier civilizations, such as the Babylonian, were 'revealed'
to them. The fact that some of the commandments can be traced
in earlier thought does not in any way invalidate this idea. Indeed
it underlines the universal nature of the moral principles incor-
porate in them. In fact, the extraordinarily universal nature of the
moral law as given in the Ten Commandments is most striking. It
is difficult to see how laws of conduct of such universal application to any society and any age could have been deduced from the
facts of human existence and experience in one nation or group of
nations in the Middle Eastern area. There is, however, a great
difference, indeed a fundamental difference, between these basic
commandments and the whole suburbia of religious rules and
scruples which grew up round the fine 'public buildings', as Jewish
history unfolded itself. These ritualistic codes, the product of the
obsessional mind, concentrating on guilt rather than on love, were
clearly demonstrated by Christ to be different in kind from the
original Commandments. As he showed it, the whole of the Ten

Commandments hinged on two – to love God on all three levels
of personality and to love one's neighbour as oneself. The more
negative commandments, 'Thou shalt not . . .', sprang from the positive ones. The keynote of all this is love. We need to look further
at what this love is, how it is allied to the emotion and to the will.

It is generally assumed that much of our Western thought, including thought about social work, is based on Christian principles.
There is a great deal of truth in this assumption. But it is also
true that just as ritualism grew up round the old Jewish law, there
has grown up round the basic teaching of Christ a suburb of 'do's'
and 'don'ts', of contentions and observances which tend to obscure
the fundamental nature of its basic declarations.

Look for a moment at some of our casework principles, in the
light of Greek and Hebrew teaching. First, that of acceptance of
the person we are trying to help. Thinking in relationalistic terms
of the origins of moral law, it is hard to see how the Greeks could
have reasoned their way to the point at which they could state
acceptance of the person as a moral principle. Take the case of a
mother who, because of her own upbringing, has little idea of how
best to bring up her child. To the Greek, to whom virtue is knowledge, she is surely unacceptable. One might say that the Greeks
would seek to enlighten her, but enlightenment could not begin
without first the acceptance.

Secondly, there is the principle of non-condemnation. This
hinges very much upon that acceptance. Non-condemnation is a
better word than non-judgment. Much of our thought about this
has been influenced by the classic injunction of Matthew's Gospel;
'Judge not, that ye be not judged'; but there is a lot more to it than
at first meets the eye. We must clear more ground then explore
further.

Thirdly, there is the principle of meeting the client's needs before one's own. I suppose some sort of empiricism might explain
the emergence of the principle. One might say that man had found,
through trial and error, through a crystallization of experience
through the ages, that society could only survive if each man put
the needs of the community before his own. But the principles of
not encouraging dependence and of *encouraging growth towards
emotional maturity* are closely linked with that of meeting the
client's needs before one's own. What that emotional maturity is,
is an extremely complex question to answer. In the New Testament, Jesus' followers are frequently told that they should be, or

should aim at becoming *teleios*. This word is frequently translated as 'perfect'; but a more accurate translation is 'mature'. This meaning may be subdivided under three heads: first, the mature man, as distinct from woman – mature in sexual relationship – not seeking a father or mother substitute; second, the mature man as distinct from the boy; this is closely linked with the first definition, but includes all the struggles out of dependency, reactions to authority and so on; and third, mature in relation to man, as distinct from God. This ties up with acceptance of our own limitations, a coming to terms with our own desire for omnipotence, our own finiteness. An analyst might say that this means a coming to terms with the infantile part of ourselves. A man who can do this can face up to the so-called 'failures' in his work in a way which will not diminish his effectiveness in other things. This third kind of maturity also prevents the arrogant interference in other people's lives of which Lady Wootton warns us, and is linked with the question of respect for the person in social work. Suffice it to say for the moment that this maturity will prevent us from trying to help people irrespective of whether they want to be helped. Christ's healing was sometimes prefaced by the question, 'Do you want to be made whole?'

Ashdown and Brown, in *Social Service and Mental Health*, speaking of the trend away from the religious impetus and outlook in social work, comment that social workers now tend to apologize if they ever admit to a simple desire to help human beings. But our principle has been defined for us, not as complete frustration of self, but as putting the client's needs before one's own. Even this goes further than the Second Commandment, which speaks of loving thy neighbour as thyself! Ashdown and Brown quote Margaret Mead: 'This whole trend towards the professionalism of service fields means a shift from an occupation to which one gives oneself – to an occupation to which one gives definite hours and specified and limited duties.'[12] Personally, I think this an over-simplification of the whole situation. The kind of self-discipline which leads the modern professional worker to confine most of his work to what may at least loosely be called 'office hours' may be a necessary and healthy thing. At least he does not become a martyr to his work. The martyr so often becomes resentful of that which eats up his whole 'self'. A neurotic drive of over-compensation for guilt may push him beyond the limits of his physical or mental strength, so that he breaks his own health and ends up unable to serve or help anyone else. Repression of a normal wish to spend some of his waking hours playing pop or classical records, meeting and talking to friends or enjoying leisure in the hundred-and-one-ways people do may cause his love and concern and the satisfaction gained in helping other people to turn to bitterness. This is not to deny that there are the few who can spend all their waking hours helping other people – and still remain loving and concerned. The secret, lies in knowing yourself, your own motivation and your own resources.

How many social workers do know their own resources and the source of the energies which drive them? Although the modern social worker generally pays lip-service to the Christian tradition underlying much of our thought and teaching, he does not seek to trace the river back to its source or to question whether this might ever dry up. If he is not a religious man, he tends to contrast what he sees as the 'blundering, ill-informed' worker of fifty years ago with the more discriminating and discerning, better-informed and more disciplined worker, the trained professional of today. He is not always aware of the dangers of social work being left a thing of techniques and theories, bereft of the spirit, emptied of the love which originally motivated it.

The nature of love in social work

What is this love? What kind of love is needed in our work? For those of us who use the English language, love is an umbrella word, embracing the sensual and the spiritual. Curiously enough, whereas the word 'erotic', in English usage, has acquired a sense almost entirely sexual (in the narrower sense of the word) one of the Greek words for love, *eros*, means something very different. *Eros* was used for the upward striving of the human soul towards the divine. It was different from the Christian word *agape* in that the object of desire had an inherent worth, which called forth the desire to possess and enjoy its object. But as Cranfield points out, it was essentially egocentric, seeking its object only for the sake of its own satisfaction and self-fulfilment. Cranfield classifies the love of some of the mystics as *eros*, in as far as they sought in God their own satisfaction and self-enhancement.[13]

When Jesus declared that on the commandment to love God and our neighbour as ourself was founded all the law, he was obviously not speaking of the love the Greeks called *eros*. His followers soon began to see that there was a great difference between *eros* and a kind of love which they began to call *agape*. This latter Greek word is to be found very little outside the New Testament and had a specific meaning for Christians. They thought of *agape* as a kind of love entirely independent of the worth of the object and in one sense utterly undemanding and unpossessive. This is what Paul emphasized when he says in his letter to the Christians in Rome, 'Even for a just man one of us would hardly die ... but Christ died for us while we were yet sinners' (Rom. 5.7f.). Christians feel that somehow a value has been set upon each and every man, which nothing we can do or be can set aside. It is not for us to question whether another human being is worthy of our love. Christ died for him. That should be enough. In the parable of the Good Samaritan, the Samaritan tended 'a certain man': not a good man, not a Jewish man, not a wealthy man, not a capitalist, nor a working man; not a kind man, not an influential man, not an attractive man, nor a pathetic-looking man, just a certain man, any man. Love independent of merit was to be shown to everyman. No one could claim to have this *agape* and love only his own kith and kin and friends, or only the attractive, the lovable, or those who could return love.

Agape is unpossessive. It is not like the love of so many of the mothers whose children land up in Child Guidance Clinics. It does not sap and frustrate the life of the one who is loved. Indeed it helps to mature that life. It does not exclude all other love. Indeed it helps to extend it. It does not demand a return of love. Indeed, it is just this which makes a response to it an act of human dignity. All these things apply to the kind of love needed in therapy. It should help to mature. It should set the person free to form better relationships with other people. It should not *require* a return of love to the therapist.

This *agape* is not an easy liking. It is a commandment. Paul says, 'Love is the fulfilling of the Law.' Edmund Spenser wrote:

> So let us love, dear love, like as we ought,
> Love is the lesson which the Lord us taught.[14]

Here again, we are up against the sense of 'oughtness' which lies at the centre of all ethics. Reinhold Niebuhr, speaking of the first two commandments, says:

Such a commandment can be understood as stating an ultimate

condition of complete harmony between the soul and God, its
neighbour and itself, in a situation in which this harmony is not
a reality. If it were a reality, the 'thou shalt' would be meaningless. If there were not some possibility of sensing the ultimate
perfection in a state of sin, the 'thou shalt' would be irrelevant.[15]

Certainly, no professional training, no increased self-knowledge,
no techniques or disciplines will make our attitudes to our clients
in social work, our patients in therapy, what they should be. Yet
the commandment is there ... the possible impossible! Tillich
points out in *Love, Power and Justice* that when we realize the
significance of the fact that we are commanded to love, we see
more clearly that the Christian idea of love must concern not only
the emotion, but also the will.[16]

The discipline of social work requires not only the desire to
heal, to make good, but the knowledge of how best to do it. Shelley
wrote 'The wise want love; and those who love want wisdom.'[17]
Part of our love for the people for whom we work shows itself
in our determination to learn, to know, all we can about human
motivation including our own and to learn the techniques of our
profession. This is the point at which will becomes linked with
emotion and we appreciate that love is a commandment.

Quite often I come across friends not professionally trained in
social work who worry because at times they feel themselves to be
hypocrites. They say that they help people or give them reassurance, or whatever else they seem to need at the moment: yet all
the time they feel they are putting on an act. They do not really
want to help that person. They do not like that person. They wish
that person had gone anywhere rather than to them. They feel
guilty because they know that what they have done to help has not
been done in the spirit in which it ought to have been done. Here
again we have the 'ought' of ethics. I do not think that the pro-
fessionally-trained person is so much worried by this particular
kind of guilt. He is much more aware of the things which have
made the person helped into an unattractive person. He is much
more aware of the reasons for his own particular reactions of
irritation or frustration. He recognizes the pattern which he has
come to acknowledge as being his particular emotional pattern.
He gives the right response to the need of the immature of the
neurotic, the depressed or the hysteric. He makes the response as
he interprets the response of love, putting, as we have so often said

before, the client's needs before his own. His own feelings at that moment are really irrelevant. If we only acted in love when we really wanted to, there are many people who would go away unhelped. The law of love is like any other law, in that there are times when we do not wish to obey it. There is a discipline about the management of our own feelings in social work. If the end result is helping other people, I do not see that it is any worse to conceal our anger from a client who would feel badly rejected if we showed it than it is to appear cheerful to our friends when we are feeling miserable but do not want to make them miserable too.

But truth and love are very closely allied. If you have a deep and abiding concern for another human being, you will strive for sincerity in your dealings with that person. Acceptance, one of the principles of casework to which we are required to remain loyal, does not always mean absence of anger, or even non-communication of anger. You need to know what is best done with your anger and what your client needs, whether letting him know about your anger is going to be destructive or helpful.

Here is an amusing illustration of the problem. A caseworker had been having weekly sessions with a twenty-three-year-old girl who had had three unwanted illegitimate children. For months part of nearly every session had been taken up with the patient's talking about her vital statistics. In getting herself pregnant she had been proving her femininity. Interpretations had been made over and over again and the patient had made a lot of progress. Yet still, relentlessly, to the point of excruciating boredom, she went on and on about her bust measurement and how her figure compared with that of other girls. Finally, the caseworker could not stand any more and said: 'For heaven's sake stop telling me about it. I am bored to death with the subject.' The patient looked at her in absolute astonishment and replied: 'But I felt I *had* to go on and on about it, because although you have helped me to understand why I used to get pregnant, I never believed you understood how *awful* I felt about it!' The therapist's outburst had somehow conveyed to the patient that there had been communication which the professional responses had to some extent disguised, and from then onwards the patient did not need to mention her bust measurement. What was needed in this situation was love in truth only, not a counterfeit version.

We have as yet barely touched upon the subject of non-condemnation in casework or therapy. R. A. Lambourne argues in

his essay 'Judgment in Psychiatry' that 'not only is moral judgment present in psychotherapy, but its presence contributes to
success'.[18] The patient in psychotherapy or the client in any close
casework relationship, if he has *any* conception of what is going
on at all, has agreed to lay his feelings and thoughts open to someone who 'makes people better'. The very fact of this role being
played by the worker implies judgment. If the client or patient
continues to attend for treatment, this is an implicit acknowledgement of the fact that he *ought* to be something different from what
he is.

A mother comes to a Child Guidance Clinic with her eleven-
year-old daughter. She has not been sent by the National Society
for the Prevention of Cruelty to Children nor by the school doctor,
nor by the Care Committee. She has come of her own free-will,
after consultation with her general practitioner. As she sits there
talking, guilt is written all over her face. Mary has a school phobia.
It is so bad that now she will not venture out of the house to go
anywhere unless her mother accompanies her. Scarcely ever does
the mother blame everything on the child. She knows that somehow, in spite of good intentions, she has been a bad mother. She
feels guilty. She expects a hostile judgment from the caseworker
and is all braced up for it. She may even say: 'I expect you will
soon be able to tell me what I have done wrong.' When, instead,
it is conveyed to her that she herself is to do the work of discovery, she becomes aware that there is no hostile judgment. But
she is still aware of judgment in the very situation. If she were not,
she would not continue to come, for she would think there was
nothing to be done, nothing that needed to be done.

In fact, there is no new discovery of self without self-judgment
and no helping the client without helping her to self-judgment.
The therapist cannot enable the patient to grow in self-knowledge,
without first sensing, to some degree, what she *ought* to be. As
therapy or casework proceeds, the patient will be encouraged to
relinquish some of her defences. The probing of these defences
and the encouraging of the patient to give them up, so that she
may live life more fully, is in itself a moral judgment. But it is a
moral judgment made in love. We can see this better, perhaps,
if we try to suppose what would happen in this situation if there
were no love. If there were no love, there would be no acceptance.
The mother would be rejected because she was a no-good mother,
perhaps a possessive mother, an over-anxious mother who does not

sufficiently well conceal her anxiety from the child. She is, in fact, a mother with the wrong kind of love for her child. But if the therapist were to reject, or deliver a hostile judgment against her, he himself would be failing in love, which we have already agreed is essential to any kind of therapy, on whatever level. If he were to accuse her, saying: 'Yes, what you think about yourself is perfectly true. You *are* a bad mother. You think mainly of what you want from your child. You are not prepared to let her become a person in her own right ...', she would go away and never come back. So a part of love is the discipline of not saying these things. His love, too, has to be of the sort which allows that mother to become a person in her own right. It is more than probable that she is what she is because she had a mother who was possessive and over-anxious. It is for the caseworker in the transference situation to break the pattern, because he knows something of a different kind of love.

The meaning of the person in social work

In a letter to Pope, Jonathan Swift wrote: 'I hate and detest that animal called Man: although I heartily love John, Peter, Thomas and so forth.' A criminal lawyer was asked how he always seemed to be able to prevent his client being hanged. He replied: 'I never speak of "my client" or "the defendant", but always Tom Jones, or Henry Brown. Juries will hang clients and defendants, but they have not the heart to hang Tom Jones or Henry Brown.'

In this day and age, as perhaps never before in history, there is what might be called a multiple store mentality, a depersonalization, a *verdinglichung*, a making of people into things. If the milk is late in the morning, instead of wondering whether Joe's wife is ill we curse the Express Dairy. In manipulating people to assuage our own desire for power, we can perhaps escape feelings of guilt by thinking of them as things rather than persons. Stephen Spender, in *The God that Failed*, a symposium written by ex-Communists, says: 'The happy Communist lives in a state of historical-materialist grace in which, instead of never seeing the wood for the trees, he never sees the trees for the wood.'[19] Physicians and surgeons talk of 'the gastric ulcer' in the corner bed and 'the tonsillectomy in bed no. 4' instead of talking about patients by name – Mrs Smith or Mr Jones. Shelley, writing of literary criticism, says that any attempt at analysis of anything has this danger, that in the analysis we may lose sight of the very essence, the life, of the whole. He speaks of putting a violet in a crucible. To find its constituent parts, it is necessary to heat it and dry it to a powder, then breaking it down into its chemical parts. In so doing, the life and beauty of the violet is irrevocably lost. The danger in dealing with people's minds is perhaps not so great, for there is nowhere they can be studied except in the living person and in his reaction to life. Yet it would be possible to find caseworkers and therapists in whom desire to analyse was too important a motive. As Wordsworth said:

> A fingering slave,
> One that would peep and botanize
> Upon his mother's grave.[20]

Respect for the 'Mrs-Smithness' of Mrs Smith shows itself in many different ways. One way which is important is in the recognition of Mrs Smith as a whole person, in the sense of her not being simply a mind. It is quite possible for workers who are intensely interested in people's minds to forget that they have a body. One psychiatrist told this story against himself. When he was still fairly new to the job, he had seen a woman patient in the middle of winter. I do not remember how the referral had been made, but it could hardly have been done through her general practitioner. He described her, with slightly agitated state, some signs of delusion. She was not seriously ill, however, and he told her to return next week, to be treated as an out-patient in the psychiatric department. Later that day, he spoke to the psychiatric social worker and asked her whether she could find time to do a home visit and take a full social history. The social worker agreed to do this and a few days later presented the finished article. Under a sub-heading 'Health' the psychiatric social worker mentioned that the thyroid condition of the patient might be relevant to her mental condition. When the patient came to see the psychiatrist it was a cold day and she came muffled up to the neck with a thick, woolly scarf. When seen by the psychiatric social worker at home, she was in a twin-set and her goitre was clearly visible. This is a rather obvious example of the kind of thing which can happen, when the psychiatrist becomes led astray by his interest and preoccupation with the patient's mind, as distinct from her body. Even if physical illness has been eliminated and casework begun, the caseworker should not automatically put down any irritation or aggression to a 'negative transference', but should be continually aware of the physical condition of the patient and alive to the possibility of the need for medical treatment.

Just as it is possible for a therapist to forget that a person is an integration of body, mind and spirit, so it is possible for a parent to forget that his or her growing child is becoming a person in his own right. The caseworker often has the task of helping the father or mother to become aware of this fact and to assist the child in this process of emotional detachment from the parent. In one case, the therapist had recommended to an over-possessive mother that her daughter, aged eleven, should have a drawer which she could lock and in which she could keep anything which she felt she wanted to keep private from the mother. The mother agreed to this, but two or three weeks later told the social worker quite blatantly that she had had a second key made, had opened the drawer and investigated the contents. She had to be helped to see that she was showing a complete disrespect for her daughter as a person. The habit of lying to a parent can sometimes, in an adolescent, be seen as an attempt to achieve independence. Because he knows something to be a lie, he knows something the parent does not know. The lies, then, are to be seen as acts which require not condemnation but understanding, in the context of this particular young person's struggle to become a person. Lying may not be a desirable means of his achieving this end, but it may well be that he has been driven to it by the frustration of all better and more satisfactory means.

One difficulty encountered by most young people as they strive to assert their own identity as persons, is that they tend to see themselves, in common with others of their age, as 'we' against 'them'. In their efforts to differentiate themselves from their parents and therefore from their parents' generation, they tend almost to lose their own identity in the crowd of their own generation. This 'ganging up' together is condemned by the parents, because it is often seen as a threat to them. In seeking deliberately to find new modes of dress and different codes of behaviour from their elders, the young seem to be passing judgment on their parents. Yet, as Dr Laycock says, 'the broad framework of society must be upheld'. What is wrong with delinquents is that they 'cannot identify themselves with the authority of the community which is exercised on their behalf'.[21]

There is, of course, in any casework, a real need for empathy.

But for a variety of reasons there are many workers who develop a predilection to identifying with one particular kind of client. Some social workers show a strong tendency to identify with the child. Others show an equally strong tendency to identify with the mother or father. Where this happens there is no real empathy with the person encountered, but merely an emotional reaction activated by the caseworker's own need to give or receive parental affection.

In dealing with other people we must take care not to confuse the need for empathy with our own inquisitiveness and desire to manipulate other human beings. Just as in a religious sphere, some evangelists try to burgle people's souls, so in the sphere of social work, some workers are tempted to force the persons with whom they are dealing either into taking some course of action which they consider desirable, or, perhaps a more subtle temptation, into giving information which is essential to the therapy. Here are two illustrations from the story of Mary who suffered from *anorexia nervosa*. In the first place, having seen her daily for six weeks, I knew, because she had told me herself, that 'something' had happened to her at the age of seven. I knew that this 'something' had overshadowed her whole life from then onwards. I also knew that this 'something' had induced in her a great fear of pregnancy; a fear which had been stirred up by more recent events to such an extent that she had decided it was dangerous to be fat and safe to be thin – as thin as she could get. To sense these things and to know that, until she had some abreaction and was able to express some of the emotion connected with the early happenings, she would not begin to get well, was a most difficult thing to contain. I was impatient to help her to get well and therefore tempted to squeeze her mentally like a tube of toothpaste. This, however, was the very thing that her mother had been apt to do and the thing against which she was most on her guard (and rightly so). Every person has a moral right to give or withhold this kind of information from another. It would be unethical to extract information by coercion, even if it were possible. Respect for the person one is trying to help is best shown by waiting until that person is ready, of her own free will, to let you in to her secret, or to let that secret out.

The second illustration of the temptation to manipulate another person came to me also in the course of the same treatment. Some weeks later, having been through the story of her struggles with the most appalling conflicts, between the ages of seven and sixteen, we reached a point at which Mary, who was a most sincere Catholic, spoke of her inability to confess any of the major events in the sequence, or any of her present sexual temptations, to her priest. The fact that she had been unable to confess was in itself a source of considerable guilt. The pathological guilt centred on her feelings about sex inhibited her and prevented her from making confession to her priest. It was really a vicious circle. Yet she seemed to have reached a point at which a formal confession would almost certainly lighten her burden of guilt and enable her to cope with it. At this point I definitely caught myself trying to persuade her to go to confession. I did not do this directly. But she had a great deal of fear of making this confession and what I actually did was to try to reduce this fear and give her a gentle shove in the right direction. I got nowhere like this – and neither did she. It was not until I learnt my lesson and accepted her fear, that we made further progress. We 'marked time' for a session or two, and the time was used in showing her that I accepted this fear of confessing. It was as if before I had been pushing and she had been counter-balancing and so pushing backwards against this move. When the point of my acceptance of the fear was reached, Mary had the opportunity to regain her balance. She was neither being pushed forwards nor pushing backwards. So she was given the chance to stand firm and look this fear in the face. Having done so, she was able of her own accord to find the courage to take this final step. She went the following week and made her confession, telling me afterwards that it had not been nearly so bad as she had expected. This was almost the final stage of her treatment. It is unethical to try to force another person to do what you know is right and good for them. It is also generally impossible.

Many modern thinkers are much occupied with the idea of the person and of the ideal of personal relationship. The slightly older idea that the goal of human endeavour is the achievement of satisfactory sexual relationships, has been replaced by the realization that the goal is the achievement of satisfactory personal relationships. Sex may well be a major means of expression of some of these relationships, but it is not the whole. Martin Buber speaks in *I and Thou* of the indifference to the establishment of true personal relationships, which is so typical of our age, the I—It relationship which so many people establish with their fellow men and women. One cannot have the compassion needed in social work in relation to a thing, but only in relation to another person.

Charlotte Towle contrasts the 'dispassionate and compassionate qualities' of the relationship between the social worker and her client;[22] the former are no less important than the latter. Although warmth is needed in the relationship, it is important to emphasize in training that too intense a relationship is not desirable. This inter-personal relationship is of a special kind. There are case-workers who, when they move on to another sphere of work, another clinic, another department, find it almost impossible to detach themselves from the clients or patients with whom they have been dealing. They may simply not prepare the client for the fact that they are leaving and another caseworker is taking over. They may just depart without a word, leaving behind a client who feels completely rejected and therefore quite unable to accept the successor. Sometimes a caseworker writes letters to clients with whom she had worked in her previous placement, striving to maintain a relationship which she does not feel able to discontinue. Both these reactions are wrong. Both show that the worker is dependent upon the affection of the client and is putting her own needs before those of the client. The caseworker has forgotten to think dispassionately.

The ethics of our dealings with other persons in social casework can be summed up as follows. Our emphasis on the professional nature of this relationship, a nature which is essential to the success of the work, should not lead us to become completely detached. We must learn to see that person as a person, to establish a good personal relationship and yet not one on which we ourselves are dependent: to see the person whole – body, mind and spirit: to respect the secrets which that person is not ready to reveal: not to manipulate or coerce, but to enable the other person to find his own way to greater freedom. The whole aim of casework, indeed, is to help persons to become more truly persons in their own right.

The law-givers and the social workers

The more our work carries us into fields of action and service where we deal with individuals as persons, the more we tend to think of any other way of looking at people or dealing with people as inferior. The social caseworker is often in danger of being a little smug and of looking down on the administrator, the politician or the statistician as one step more removed from reality and therefore as inhuman or as a theorist. But if the social services are to develop towards the greater good of these persons with whom we deal, there is a crying need, indeed necessity, that the worker should be able to take a wide view, to be able to see the whole *Weltgeschicht* and not to think of himself as one of the chosen people who alone are able to set all things right. The social worker himself must develop new skills in group and community work. He must continually acknowledge that there are conscientious people, co-operative people, highly-skilled people, concerned people, at every level, executive and administrative. Baldwin once called upon the Civil Service to 'remember the idiosyncrasies of men'. Perhaps they need reminding, but some of them do remember. And if we want to play the best part we can in the social services and help influence their future, we must be more aware and more appreciative than most social workers are of the vital part played by the statisticians, the economists and the administrators. It is only by so doing that we can effect what is necessary to help to make the law what it ought to be, or in Mrs K. McDougall's delightful phrase 'to apply therapy to the law'.

The adaptation of the law is a perennial process and works from the particular to the general. The social worker deals with the individual, the administrator at local levels adds up 'caseloads', or counts families helped, the statistician makes histograms and enables the minister to inaugurate legislation. Dickens said: 'The law is an ass.' But this is not always so, and where it is, it may be partly our fault. The law does try to ensure fair distribution of resources. It is informative, but it can be so, in the final run of things, only because we have been informative in the first place.

When we consider our own position in relation to the law, there are many aspects which we have to remember. Much of the law applies to the normal person rather than to the abnormal. Law tends to be formulated in terms of the greatest good for the greatest number. Only part of the law is preventive, in that it is designed to protect the weak against the possible onslaughts of aggressive members of society. Some of it is informative, in that it is designed to tell us that if we adopt certain procedures, we might do damage to certain sections of the community.

Frequently we, identifying with our clients to a greater or lesser extent, will consider that the Department of Health and Social Security is being exceptionally mean: that the allowances permitted for this particular kind of case are insufficient: that this is an exceptional case'. Here again, we may be up against our own desire for omnipotence in a subtly-disguised form. We may be wanting to play the part of the good mother (or good father) who is able to see that the family is adequately provided for. Continually we are up against the fact that the economic cake, from which our clients are to have a slice, is of a size conditioned by the whole economic structure of the country. There is only so much to go round. Remembering Kant's Categorical Imperative – 'Act only on that principle which thou canst at the same time will to become universal law' – it is as well to remember the reverse side. If only so much is possible for the community as a whole, only so much is going to be possible for us and for our clients. Most social workers have to work long hours, because only a certain number can be employed. There is no money for more. We may feel a certain moral indignation against the state, or the local authority, that this is so. Perhaps the Exchequer's allocation of money is wrong: there should be less given to ... what? ... the Arts? ... Defence? ... the National Health Service? ... and more to the social services? If there is a good case for a claim for a bigger proportion of the nation's expenditure, some of the workers who are completely engrossed in their caseloads may have to give up some of their precious hours to prove this to the statisticians and administrators.

Social work consciences may be more sensitive than they used to be. Not so many years ago caseworkers were apt to concentrate on helping a client come to terms with things – impossible housing conditions, insufficient amenities and the rest. Adjustment was the catchword; not quite 'God bless the squire and his relations, and keep us in our proper stations', but pretty close to it. Now we are acutely aware that because we hear from people who themselves are struggling with ghastly problems, because we can actually see them doing it, we should be contributing to the amelioration of conditions. Men and women in many other jobs can plead ignorance and so justify non-action. We cannot. We are in the privileged position of seeing and hearing first-hand. Thomas à Kempis said: 'The more thou knowest and the better thou understandest, the more strictly shalt thou be judged.' The message is applicable to us.

More money is not always the answer to problems. Section I of the 1963 Children's Act has solved some problems and created others. Easy access to money tempts social workers to perpetuate dependency. Good social work often means good economy for the country as a whole, or for the borough. Miss Shapiro quotes a most striking example of this. In Birmingham in the 1950s an experiment was made in which the Housing Department and the psychiatric social workers employed by the local authority co-operated. One hundred and forty-four families with children under seven were referred to the social workers. They were all in danger of eviction because they had not paid their rent. The social workers chose to work with forty of the families. These were by no means the best bets. But in twelve months' work the workers collected £700 in arrears and the current rent. If the tenants had been evicted and two hundred children taken into care, the cost to the authority would have been about £1,000 per week.[23] At that time the annual salary of each caseworker would have been about £1,000; so that two weeks' work saved Birmingham the cost of their salaries! Sound economics. Sound ethics. What matters most is not how much money is saved in a year, but how many people's lives are made bearable.

Administrators are not unaware that there is not only an economic but also a moral side to the question of allocation of public money. A County Council's Association memorandum of 1960 states that in many homes deprived of a father and therefore of a bread-winner, the mothers are 'devoted mothers from whom it would be most undesirable to separate their children'. One mother with three small boys attended a Child Guidance Clinic for a short while. The middle boy needed help in adjusting to home, after an unsettling time in care. The young mother had been deserted by her husband and had had to go out to work to support herself: the boys were in care for two years. Then a child care officer persuaded the local council to give the mother a council flat. She was given sufficient money to pay the rent and keep her three boys. An excellent mother, who treated the boys with the right mixture of firmness, kindness and humour, she did not need clinic assistance for long, and had the sense to ensure that the boys had regular contact with adult male friends who could act as some sort of father-substitute. On her first visit to the clinic, however, she said that there had been trouble soon after the boys returned to live with her. The child care officer had helped her to get established in her own home once more and had encouraged her to keep her boys with her. But the official from the Department of Health and Social Security had tried to persuade her to go out to work, so that she could earn enough to manage without benefits. It is doubtful whether the latter was aware how foolish this was, both from a short-term and a long-term point of view. There were no close relatives to look after the children and the council had given this family the flat on the understanding that the mother did not go out to work. If she had done so, the family would have been disrupted once more. The children would have been taken back into care and deprived not only of their father but also once more of their mother. From a financial point of view, the cost of that broken home would have been many times the present cost of social security benefits. And what would be the future prospect of those children making good homes of their own in adult life? Here, it seems, economics and ethics go hand in hand. The ministries concerned with these problems have been aware of tug-of-war situations for some time. A joint circular of the Ministries of Health and Education, issued in July 1950, stated: 'The relieving officer may be pressing the wife to go out to work while the health visitor is persuading her to stay at home.' The formation of the new Social Services Departments, in which social workers will be working in area teams, may solve some of these problems. But education, housing, health and social security officials are not yet to be part of these teams.

Members of disturbed and insecure families encourage and perpetuate rivalries, suspicions and lack of co-operation between social work agencies. They demand attention and use anyone who allows himself to be used. Some are extraordinarily good at manipulation of social workers. What the families so often play upon is the conviction of many workers that they alone are enlightened, they alone are capable of waving a magic wand and converting the problem family into a model one! This is part of the omnipotence fantasy discussed earlier. It is unethical to allow oneself to be used in this kind of way. In the first place, it is a waste of time and money. The situation is worsened, not improved, by the continued involvement of so many social workers and administrators. The people who should be helped are not helped. Professional people should not allow themselves to be so used. In training we should learn to do those things which require doing and acquire knowledge of circumstances which need to be discovered and not waste our time (if we can call it our time) on enquiring into the irrelevant, however interesting and spicy the details may be.

There are tensions and rivalries between the social caseworker and the administrator. We must, however, believe that to some extent the aims of the two are identical. Both are aiming at increasing the happiness or the self-fulfilment of other people. But whereas the administrator and politician concentrate generally on the greatest good for the greatest number, the social worker tends to concentrate on the happiness of certain individuals. Very often these individuals represent minority groups within the community.

The state cannot entirely prevent people from harming themselves or others. It cannot prevent people from marrying partners who will not build with them the marital relationships they need. It often cannot prevent people from using too great a proportion of their money on the wrong things, for example, alcohol or hire-purchase. Only in notified cases can it prevent people from being cruel to their children. The law can, however, ensure a minimum standard of living standard for all, a standard which is, in this country, at least above starvation level. It does ensure that education and medical services are available to all. There have recently been some extremely important moves in the field of what we call preventive medicine. It would be difficult to draw a line between social reform and preventive medicine. Industrial legislation prevents employers from exploiting their workers by making them work too long hours or under conditions detrimental to their health. Much of our social legislation aims at freeing the greatest possible number of people from fear and from want.

Dr Laycock in his essay 'Ethics and Social Work' says: 'The reason why permissiveness is of the essence of the social work, is that what is done under coercion ... leaves an individual fundamentally unchanged and no more capable of a fuller life than he was before.'[24] Yet we do not have to look very deeply into the social structure of the country to realize that on a national scale, coercion, the imposing of law, is essential to a society which aims at ensuring the maximum possible freedom for its people. Anarchy could never lead to the freedom of the individual. In saying this we assume that the way of life in which he can fulfil himself is that which is conducive to the happiness of the whole community. Nevertheless, from what we have already said, we can see that laws do not fundamentally change men. Dr Fosdick has said that law is like a pump. It pumps up clean or dirty water, according to what is there.[25] However good the laws may be, if men do not see why they need to obey them, or if they think it will be of greater benefit to them personally not to obey them, they will not obey them.

People who have an extremely high moral standard and those who, consciously or not, are most highly tempted, frequently desire most to punish others through the medium of the law. Although statistics have not proved that capital punishment is a deterrent to a would-be murderer, many in positions of authority, because of basic fears and aggression aroused in them by the thought of murder, continue to say that it must be a deterrent. Statistics should be read with compassion. They can be read with aggression. The motivation of the legislator is just as important as the motivation of the social worker.

There is a new and important link between the poorer, ill-educated and inadequate client and his legislators. Because such a large proportion of the money drawn in from taxation is now spent on the health and social services, there is a growing tendency for the professional classes to use them. They are much more closely involved than they used to be, and therefore more prone to use their influence to get the law adapted where they think it needs adapting. Sometimes there is self-interest in this; sometimes not. Views are expressed through questions in the House of Commons, letters to *The Times*, and through the 'old-boy' network, where pressures can still be exerted and influence really felt. Whether we think it fair or not, things still happen this way. In spite of universal suffrage and compulsory education, however, it remains true that those most in need of the social services are those who have least say in the provisions for them. This is why it is vitally important to clear and deepen the channels of communication between client, social worker, administrator and legislator, and why I emphasize that it is unethical for the social worker to remain in an ivory-tower of one-to-one casework or of group work. He must get out into the community. He must find out what people need in order to prevent crises from happening. Then he must find a way of making his voice heard in his local authority and in Parliament, while encouraging and enabling people to see that their own conditions are improved.

The social worker, also for another reason, needs continually to play his part in the making of new legislation. Emil Brunner, one of the great modern theologians, defined heresy as 'truth pursued to its logical conclusion'. Human lives do not always follow neat patterns. Their details cannot always be fitted into histograms. Laws conceived entirely from the study of statistics might steamroller in the most unethical way over the happiness and the basic rights of individuals. Law needs to be humanized by the exceptions to it. The state needs continually to be reminded that it should agonize over decisions in which the individual is sacrificed to the good of the community. A local authority has plans for re-housing, which involve the demolition of a block of slum dwell-ings. One old lady of ninety remains in one of those almost derelict houses. She refuses to move to an old people's home because she is convinced she would be miserable there. She says she will move only if the local authority offers her a bed-sitting room. This accommodation is not available at the moment. So, the rehousing of fifty people is held back out of respect for the feeling of one old lady. Many might point out that there are children at risk among the fifty whose rehousing is delayed by the Housing Com-mittee's decision. But who is to say glibly what is the ethical deci-sion – to evict, or not to evict?

Individual happiness and fulfilment often conflicts with the needs of the community. The Greeks knew all about this problem and it will always be with us. It serves to remind us – as we con-tinually need reminding – that we are not omnipotent. We can only glimpse the ideal and be content to achieve the possible.

Knowledge and feeling: the code and the spirit

The law cannot change men fundamentally. It can prevent or punish extremes of violence or crime, but it cannot raise the moral standard of a nation. Can the 'techniques' of social work fundamen-tally change us? We have looked at the sources of our principles of social casework and at the nature of love needed in therapy. But what about the actual methods by which, as caseworkers, we are taught to work with our clients? Bertha Reynolds has raised the question whether casework can be learnt as a technique. 'A tech-nique', she says, 'is the best way of doing something, learnt by repeated practice and performed without substantial variation.' She adds 'Techniques are appropriate for activities which lend them-selves to standardization and in which originality of method is wasteful, rather than desirable ... Social work has had relatively few procedures which could be standardized.'[26] If we agree with Miss Reynolds' definition of technique, we would agree that the term is too narrow to cover the methods of work which we adopt. We cannot, in fact, learn a set of techniques which will enable us to help people in every situation.

These methods which we study and which we try to apply to our own efforts to help others are based on the broad principles of acceptance and respect for others. The importance of our training consists in the opportunity to work out the real meaning of these principles and the consequences of applying them. With this goes the opportunity to practise methods of dealing with people, with their reactions and one's own – methods which result from the holding of these principles. To a certain extent, this is a logical and disciplined process, distinct from the more haphazard and emotional working of the non-professional. But our profession is a very new one. The concept of casework, as something with recognizable methods, has developed only during this century. We are not yet sufficiently well-established as 'professionals' to feel secure. This is one reason why social workers tend to be over-sensitive to criticism from other groups of professional people. This makes the need for research work in these fields all the greater. John Rickman defines the quack in two ways ... as 'one who has not submitted to a course of training regarded as adequate by the teachers in a profession; who makes no consistent endeavour to integrate any discovery he may make in the exercise of the profession to the body of knowledge already existing.'[27]

It seems to me that much of the importance of our training in casework lies in the systematization of our thinking. To have a very detailed and profound self-knowledge would be of little use, if you were not continually to remind yourself of your own biases which might influence your relationship with your client and your reaction to what he tells you. A ready recognition of the traps into which you are likely to fall, or ways in which the client might try to manipulate you, is essential. A 'theory' of casework helps here. It is a kind of skeleton on which each of us can hang the covering of his or her personality and belief and experience. The casework principles are basic, whether they are backed by religious belief or some kind of humanism. Social work students of each generation accept them at first on trust (sometimes with distrust!) and prove them by experience. As Rickman says, the essentials of an ethical approach to a profession are 'willingness to learn with due humility from an older generation and to give without arrogance to the next'.[28]

The social worker is well-trained if he has learnt to integrate completely into his own thought and action the casework methods which he has studied. He must first accept what is really a system of thought. Then he must learn to live and breathe it – at least during working hours. He must know how to use, as a tool in his trade, what he has been taught from others' experience. If he is well-trained, he will always to some extent remain aware that he is using it. Yet he will use this skill, this tool, in such a way that the client will not become over-conscious of it. Margaret Knight, in *William James*, quotes the well-known saying: 'The good golfer plays a difficult stroke and makes it look easy. The bad golfer plays an easy stroke and makes it look difficult.'[29] Just how you put over to a particular client what ought to be your relationship to him will depend a good deal on your own personality and on his.

However excellent your training may be, you cannot become a successful caseworker without conviction. By conviction, I do not mean merely an intellectual thing, but something which involves your deepest feelings. In considering what kind of love is needed in therapy we have discussed how an undisciplined love is of no avail, if it is given in the wrong place and withheld in the wrong place. On the other hand, to know where this 'right kind of love' should be given and yet not to possess it in order to give is surely worse. Of course our discipline will for the most part carry us over those periods when we feel we hate the sight of every client:

> I wish I loved the human race.
> I wish I loved its silly face.
> I wish I loved the way it walked.
> I wish I loved the way it talked.
> And when I met another one,
> I wish I thought 'What jolly fun!'

We all have these moments or these days. Sometimes we have to work with clients through times of the bitterest personal disappointments or upheaval in private life. Having a real feeling for people and being disciplined to put their need before your own, we do our best to get through these periods. But it is better to start with the feeling and learn to discipline it than to start with a rational appreciation of the need for social casework and then try to work up the feeling for it. This is getting things the wrong way round, like the little scientists in *Gulliver's Travels* who spent all their days trying to discover how to get sunshine out of cucumbers. First find the warmth, the desire to help people, then learn the theory of how best to do it.

One's own warmth of love for others and one's own respect for them as persons is often greatly increased by contact with other professionals who have it. I remember being impressed as a student by seeing the courtesy with which a doctor treated mentally ill patients, or the concern with which a senior psychiatric social worker treated awkward mothers, or the way in which both discussed their work at a case-conference. When there are students about, trained workers try to maintain a high standard in order to give them a good pattern of behaviour to follow. I do not think we can over-estimate the effect of the way in which our professional behaviour towards those we are trying to help influences the students who observe us. Influence is a very powerful thing; and a very subtle thing. Our example of acting towards a person as we ought to do will have far more effect on the untrained worker who looks on than any amount of quotation from Gordon Hamilton. The creating of atmosphere in our particular agency is an important aspect of our work. One finds oneself 'warmed' by the best in the professional workers around one. Once trained, the great problem is how to maintain one's own vision of what ought to be. One may perhaps retain the casework theory, but it is not always so easy, in some settings, to retain the warmth.

Warmth matters, then; but perhaps one's own personal 'carrying-out' of the moral code does not. For instance, it may not matter whether a social worker is living with someone else's wife, or husband. It may not matter what a social worker's philosophy is, or what his religion is, or whether he has none. We might expect a religious person to say that it does matter; but experience proves otherwise. Often a client or family does not know, after several months, what the worker's beliefs are, or how he lives. It is not necessary for the success of the work that he should know. I make one very important proviso here, though. It is that whatever happens in the worker's private life does not embitter him or fill him with guilt or weaken him, so that these feelings run over into his professional life. Theoretically, in a well-trained worker this would not happen. 'Ought' and 'is' are never quite the same thing, however, and so theory and practice do not entirely coincide. Looking solely at the ethics of social work, the important thing is that your private life should not be allowed to injure your professional work. Take an analogy in surgery. A surgeon might bully his wife and cheat the income tax people, but his work might not suffer in the least. He would still be able to save lives. But if he started to drink heavily or spent every night out on the tiles, his hand would shake and his vision be impaired. Then it would matter to the patient what kind of life his surgeon was leading. Each of us can think of parallel circumstances in social work.

A (rather verbose) writer reporting on the 1960 Keele Conference, said: 'Some Social Workers might feel with some justification that the urgency of performing these acts of service was greater than the urgency of ensuring scrupulous logicality in the formation of their moral and philosophical views.' In plain words, social workers might feel it was more important to get on with the job than to explore the reasons why. In the past, social workers have been the practical people; now, with increased opportunity for casework and group work and community work, we need also to become something of philosophers. But remember Romeo's words in *Romeo and Juliet*,

> Unless philosophy can make a Juliet,
> Displant a town, reverse a prince's doom,
> It helps not, it prevails not.

There must be purpose in any philosophizing we do. It ought to be undertaken because we want to become better social workers. We must not allow ourselves to retreat into theorizing. Professor Jeffries warns: 'If we can see ourselves as thinkers, we can the more easily excuse ourselves from doing anything.'[30] Herein lies the great difficulty. Philosophers are not generally also practical men. They therefore tend to develop their ideas from theory to theory, rather than from practice to theory. This is why the practical worker so often complains that they have nothing to say which can really help him in his work.

To quote Professor Nowell-Smith again: 'Granted that men are what McDougall or Freud or Adler tell us that they are, nothing whatever follows as to what they ought to be.'[31] But there is a sense in which facts have significance in moral judgment. R. F. Atkinson, a moral philosopher, puts it to us that many moral judgments can be seen as 'reasoned injunctions to people to behave in certain ways.'[32] It makes sense to tell someone he should act in such-and-such a way only if he could. Moral philosophy would be dealing only with a world of fantasy if it were concerned solely with the impossible; it could have nothing worthwhile to say to us. Economists not only tell us the present state of man: they propound theories about how this state could be improved. Psychologists and sociologists must do the same.

Nevertheless the converse of our statement about what men are and what they ought to be is also true: granted that men ought to be what the moral philosopher tell us they ought to be, nothing whatever follows as to what they are. Theory in itself will not make men and women into better human beings – or us into better social workers. Our great problem is how to become more what we ought to be. Going through the motions does not necessarily arouse the emotions. An unmaternal mother breast-feeding a child and holding it close does not always find within herself an increase of warmth and love towards the child. Indeed she may grow to hate it. We cannot learn to love and respect people simply by acting as though we do.

Looking at the concept of love needed in therapy, we saw it not as an easy liking of the attractive or of people who can fulfil some need in ourselves, but as a commandment which is often hard to obey. To the religious person, it is seen as commanding heart, mind and soul: or we might say in psychological terms, emotion, reason and will. We have discussed the discipline of this love, on off-days and in moments of irritation and moments of desire to reject a client or a family. But although the discipline of the will, which increases with greater self-knowledge, will carry us through these periods, we know that it alone will not make our work what it ought to be. There must be a commitment on the emotional level as well – a controlled emotion, but none the less an emotion, a warmth. We talk a great deal about helping people towards maturity. For growth a plant needs both light and heat. The increased understanding which we give someone we help is 'light'. But for growth he needs also warmth. It is no good simply going through the motions of being a good caseworker or group worker or community worker. It is no good grunting at the right moments. It is no good disciplining oneself not to criticize. It is no good knowing all there is to know of theories of human motivation. It is no good being fully conversant with the 'techniques' of our profession. None of these is of any avail unless the social worker has also warmth. The law is of no use without the spirit.

Philosophy behind the development of the social services
How do they progress?

I said in my preamble that ethics is not primarily concerned with the actual characteristics of human behaviour, but with its ideals.

I also said that in talking of a social science, we were dealing with a specialized form of knowledge; and that any science worthy of the name dealt not only with what 'is' but also with what 'is possible', or 'could be'. If our knowledge points us onward from what now is to what is possible, then 'possible' becomes the new 'is' and progress is made. In the field of economics, old age pensions and a National Health Service only became foreseeable possibilities with the establishment of heavy taxation. So the economic structure of the country was adapted step by step, always one step ahead of the social services. There are many evolutionary theories of ethics and we need to look at some of them.

Darwin, whose theories cut so deeply into the structure of all previous thought about living things, believed that the instincts and habits which contributed to the survival of animal life developed into moral qualities which tended to the preservation of human life. The empiricists' case-law of life, a crystallization of the discoveries man has made in his attempt to adapt to his environment, can be seen to tally with Darwin's theories about survival of the fittest. Natural selection influences the growth from purely tribal morality into morality as we know it in its more complex forms. Herbert Spencer spelt this out more clearly. He said he believed it to be 'the business of moral science to deduce from the laws of life and the conditions of existence what kinds of actions necessarily tend to produce happiness and what kinds to produce unhappiness'. He seemed to make ethics wait upon a complete knowledge of biology and its allied sciences.

Among European thinkers, Nietzsche alone carried the idea of evolutionary ethics to its logical conclusion. The conclusion is such a terrible one that one hardly likes to use the word 'ethics' to cover it. The 'ethical' code of Nietzsche, involving the survival of the fittest, means the disappearance of love, sympathy, tolerance and all altruistic ideals (save, perhaps, the one of the 'altruism' of the weak, who presumably allow themselves to be exterminated by the strong). A bare statement of such a philosophy must make us ask certain questions about our own ethical standards. Can we reconcile our own moral philosophy with a move towards preservation of the race? Why do we protect the weak – and is it 'good' to do so? If problem families breed problem families and psychopathic parents tend to produce delinquent children, why not eliminate the lot? Why not run the steam-roller of the state over them, put them into concentration camps and gas-ovens? Apart from a simple restatement of the basic teachings of Jesus, what answer have we?

There is probably only one other answer. It is that of existentialism. And although there are many agnostics and so-called atheists among existentialists, from Kierkegaard onwards the origins of much of their thinking lie in the Christian faith. Heinemann, in *Existentialism and the Modern Predicament*, argues that the philosophy reflected a movement in bourgeois society which, in response to the challenge of collectivism implied in Socialism, Bolshevism and Fascism, attempted to save the person within a society of free persons. He says: 'The Bolshevists hate the existentialists as the potential revolutionaries of the future. In fact the existentialists are philosophers of resistance. They attempt to resist the collectivizing trend, bound up with machine production, which seems to lead in any society, whether fascist, democratic or socialist, to a depersonalization of man.' Existentialists from Kierkegaard to Marcel have protested 'against the absorption of man by the machinery of the modern welfare state ... the extension of the power of the state and the substitution of the registration card for the person.[33] These modern philosophers react against the all-pervading power of the state. Tillich believes that what they oppose is the 'system of thought and life developed by Western industrial society and its philosophical representatives, ... a logical or naturalistic mechanism which seemed to destroy individual freedom, personal decision and organic community; an analytic rationalism which spans the vital forces of life and transforms everything, including man himself, into an object of calculation and control; a secularized humanism which cuts man off from the creative source and the ultimate mystery of existence.' Heinemann's comment on this is: 'If the existentialist reminds us of the dangers inherent in a technological civilization and of the necessity of having roots, he may fulfil a function vital for the survival of man.'[34]

The Renaissance was the time of emphasis on the individual. In our time, existentialism, reacting as it does against the technocratic view of man, is placing new emphasis on the importance of the person in the community. Men depend upon each other. Men influence one another. Marcel and others keep saying what has been reiterated in this article: that the maturity of the person is to be judged by the achievement of successful relationships with other people. For instance, a deprived eight-year-old in a large school is above average in spelling and arithmetic, a model pupil.

But he is withdrawn and shy and has no friends. As a pupil he is a success; as a person he is a failure. Of personal fulfilment and happiness he knows practically nothing. What applies to the school applies to the modern state. It is possible to be a citizen who creates no problems for others, but who has found none of the secrets of life.

Where deterministic philosophies hold sway, man is transformed into 'an object of calculation and control'. The Communist thinks of men and women as motivated and controlled by economic forces, with which they must conform or cease to exist. The glib catchword 'From each according to his ability: to each according to his need' sounds fine until one begins to question who is to decide another man's need. Is it to be the person himself, or the local commissar, or the Politburo? In politics there is no easy answer. Neither is there in social work. Who is to assess the client's need? Is it to be the client, his wife and family, the Housing Department, the tenants' association, Department of Health and Social Services, or the social worker?

If all developments in the social structure are dependent upon deterministic forces, there is no such thing as choice. Changes in legislation, alterations in the way persons are treated within the community, by the community, will take place, because of the sequence of events preceding them, because of the facts of the present, rather than because there is any goal ahead. What we call ethical naturalism comes close to this, when it states that moral judgments can be deduced from factual statements. If this were so, it would mean that moral goodness and rightness could be defined in purely factual terms, such as satisfaction, adjustment or social welfare. If this were so, it would be possible to offer scientific proofs of moral judgments.

If our philosophy were to become deterministic, we would tend more and more to deny the possibility of any moral choice. Then the word ethics would become completely meaningless. One cannot deny that facts about human motivation discovered during the last fifty to a hundred years have considerably modified our moral judgments. The vast majority of men and women who commit anti-social acts are still held responsible for their own decisions and are considered to be able to make a right choice in preference to a wrong one. But let us not forget how far our new knowledge about human motivation has caused us to modify our laws and adapt our social services. We already have special places of custody

for criminal psychopaths. We have a few special residential units
for alcoholics. We have special departments in some prisons for
the re-education of parents accused of neglecting and ill-treating
their children. New facts learnt, in other words a modified picture
of 'what is', have caused us to modify our actions. This does not
mean that they have actually modified our social ethic. We still
believe that brutality to children, murder and rape are wrong. We
judge differently the persons who commit these crimes and treat
them according to what we at present believe to be best for them
and for the community.

The deterministic philosophy of a Communist state has much
in common with the philosophy of Nietzsche. The survival of the
fittest means to the Marxist the survival of the proletariat. The
Communist worker believes this principle to be the crystallization
of the experience of workers. It is empirical. But it is also non-
ethical. There is no question of 'right' and 'wrong', but what is
expedient and what is not expedient. This thinking affects the
development of the social services in a Communist state. It
accounts for the treatment of old people and others who are not
able to contribute to the welfare of the community. An examination of the philosophy and of its effects on the social system can
enable us to see more clearly how ours differs. In adapting our own
system to provide for the needs of the old, the mentally and physically handicapped and persons who for other reasons are not themselves contributing to the welfare of the state, we are doing
something which is essentially ethical. While maintaining still that
every person can best fulfil himself in service to the community
and in satisfactory relationships, we yet do not discard those who
are not fully able to do this. We aim to provide for them, too,
within our system – however inadequately. This is partly because
our ethical system embraces convictions about respect for the
person. It is in essence existentialist. It is a response to a conviction. Heinemann says: 'I am, in so far as I respond.' Man's evolution consists of interrelated and complicated acts of response. But
this is no mere behaviourism. 'With the rise of consciousness, the
purely mechanical circle is broken. We become conscious as to
how we are reacting or how we should respond.' This, you will see,
is very close to our conception of increased maturity, as aimed at
in casework. Heinemann says: 'Though determined by the stimuli
we are free in the manner in which we respond and at liberty not to
respond at all beyond the sphere of merely mechanical reaction.'[35]

Part of the idea of response lies in the concept of thought possessing a living quality. We may call a thought 'alive' if it produces activity and organizes human behaviour. This links up very well with what we were saying about the dangers of mere theorizing. An ethic has no living quality unless it is worked out in the life of the community, and we are thinking particularly of the ways in which it is worked out in social service.

We spoke of theorizing. It is a fallacy that knowledge is virtue. The knowledgeable man is not necessarily the good man. But people who are going to undertake a practical job of helping people will be the better for thinking about the why and wherefore of it. Does theorizing help us to play the best part we can in society? This depends on whether we are indulging ourselves by theorizing about something remote, or whether we are thinking about something we are already practising and to which we are already committed. We have to remember also that theory is always general; we, in the end, have to act in particular situations. This applies whether we are social workers or legislators. In the theory we learn something about our goals from which we acquire a sense of direction as we play our part in the development of our services. Human life being what it is, the goals must always be beyond our reach. If it were not so, we would arrive and no longer have to travel hopefully. We would find and no longer have to seek. We would have attained omniscience and omnipotence and no longer have to strive. Then we would have ceased to be men and women, the finite, restricted creatures we are.

R. F. Atkinson, in the article already quoted, says that many practically-minded people believe that practical workers in the helping professions need the support of faith.[36] It may be a religious one; or it may be faith in the tenets of psycho-analytical theory; or it may be faith in the eventual triumph of Communism. I believe it to be true that a faith gives impetus to action. It helps to sustain the spirit in which we would like always to work. We could argue eternally about whether the good within men is self-perpetuating or whether it needs continual reactivation by a divine goodness. History seems to tell us that creative human thought – and action – needs some kind of fuel. We must draw upon some source of power or we quickly use up all warmth and energy. We must be for ever confronted with an ideal which questions every minute-by-minute reaction, each daily decision, each committee finding, each Parliamentary debate, binding all into a meaningful

whole. Maturity in our social system, as in our personal lives, can
only come from a vision of an impossible goal.

A man's reach must exceed his grasp,
Or what's a Heaven for?

NOTES

1. P. H. Nowell-Smith, 'Ethics and Psychology', *Sociological Review
Monograph* (cited hereafter as *Soc. Rev. Mon.*) 3, Keele, 1960, p.15.

2. D. V. Donnison, 'Reform and Therapy,' *Soc. Rev. Mon.* 3, 1960, p.45.

3. Barbara Wootton, *Social Science and Social Pathology*, Allen and
Unwin 1959, p.279.

4. Elizabeth Howarth, 'An Introduction to Casework Supervision', *Case
Conference* 8.6, Welwyn, November 1961, p.160.

5. Gordon Hamilton, author of *Social Case Recording*, Columbia University Press 1936, etc.

6. Paul Tillich, *Love, Power and Justice*, Oxford University Press 1954,
p.29.

7. Karen Horney, *The Neurotic Personality of our Time*, Routledge and
Kegan Paul 1937.

8. Margaret Ferard, 'Psychiatric Social Work and Social Casework in
other Fields', *Boundaries of Casework: a Symposium*, Association of Psychiatric Social Workers 1956, p.18.

9. A. L. Laycock, 'Ethics and Social Work', *Case Conference* 8.6, November 1961, p.153.

10. D. V. Donnison, art. cit., p.53.

11. Charlotte Towle, *The Learner in Education for the Professions*, University of Chicago Press 1967, p.62.

12. Margaret Ashdown and Sybil Clement Brown, *Social Service and
Mental Health*, Routledge and Kegan Paul 1953, p.221.

13. C. E. B. Cranfield, art. 'Love', in *A Theological Word Book of the
Bible*, ed. Alan Richardson, SCM Press 1950, pp.133ff.

14. Edmund Spenser, *Sonnet* 68.

15. Reinhold Niebuhr, *The Nature and Destiny of Man*, I. Nisbet 1941,
p.303.

16. *Tillich*, op. cit., pp.4f.

17. Shelley, *Prometheus Unbound* I, 627.

18. R. A. Lambourne, 'Judgment in Psychiatry', *Frontier* 4, Summer
1961, p.110.

19. Stephen Spender in *The God that Failed*, ed. R. H. S. Crossman,
Bantam Books, New York, 1959, p.233.

20. Wordsworth's, 'A Poet's Epitaph'.

21. Laycock, art. cit., p.154.

22. Charlotte Towle, op. cit., p.314.

23. P. Shapiro, 'The Caseworker, the Welfare Officer and the Administrator in the Social Services: I', *Boundaries of Casework*, pp.78f.

24. Laycock, art. cit., p.154.

25. H. E. Fosdick, *On Being Fit to Live With*, Harper and Bros., New
York, 1946, p.37.

26. Bertha Reynolds, *Learning and Teaching in the Practice of Social
Work*, Farrar and Rinehart, New York, 1942.

27. John Rickman, 'Psychology in Medical Education', *British Medical Journal* 6 September 1947, p.365 note.

28. Loc. cit.

29. Margaret Knight, *William James*, Pelican 1950, p.46.

30. M. V. C. Jeffreys, 'Commitment and Objectivity', *Soc. Rev. Mon.* 3, 1960, p.80.

31. P. H. Nowell-Smith, art. cit., p.15.

32. R. F. Atkinson, 'Some Philosophical Issues arising in Professional Training', *Soc. Rev. Mon.* 3, 1960, p.148.

33. F. H. Heinemann, *Existentialism and the Modern Predicament*, A. and C. Black 1953, p.167.

34. Ibid., p.26, quoting Tillich, 'Existential Philosophy', in *Journal of the History of Ideas* V. 1, 1944, pp.44ff.

35. Ibid., pp.192f.

36. Atkinson, art. cit., p.151.

6 The Pastoral Role: A Psychiatrist's View

James R. Mathers

Dr Mathers was formerly Medical Superintendent of Rubery Hill (Psychiatric) Hospital, Birmingham.

This chapter is based on a paper read at a conference on 'The Further Training of Clergy' organized by the Department of Extramural Studies, University of Birmingham on 21 April 1971.

The image of the shepherd is not the most obvious of conceptual models for our twentieth-century urban society. As I started to prepare this essay, I was startled to remember that not so many years ago I used to feel a repugnance towards the use of the word pastoral in an ecclesiastical context: it seemed to have a rather cloying sense of arcadian sentimentality which seemed ill-fitted to express the caring functions within a body of men dedicated to so tough a task, so ultimate an adventure, as the search for the kingdom of God. Nowadays I have grown familiar with the word and it no longer offends me; but I do not suppose I am unique and it may well continue to be a stumbling block to other laymen. However, I will not be so rash as to suggest an alternative here.

The close relationship between pastor and priest with which we are familiar is, if we take a long perspective, unexpected. We may speculate that the primitive social group, seeking for better ways by which to deal with its experiences of evil, allowed the differentiation of the original medicine-man or witch-doctor into three clearly distinguishable (though not necessarily separate) roles – those of ruler, priest and healer.[1] Of the three, the first two would be more concerned with public or corporate problems, while the healer would be expected to deal more with private and individual evils. The emergence of the pastoral concept in Israel seems logically enough to have been more closely associated with the ruler or kingly role (Cf. Ezek. 34). Even though the kings of Israel may have had priestly functions it was as rulers rather than as priests that they would earn the title of shepherd. It was the ruler's task to care for his people; that of the priest was to preserve and teach the tradition.

The increased emphasis on the care of people in trouble and on the healing of the sick, which is to be found in the teaching of Jesus, certainly justified the early church in paying greater attention to its pastoral functions; and it may well be that the historical circumstances precluded any hope at that time of maintaining a credible link between the pastoral and ruling roles. But neither Jesus nor Paul would seem to have contemplated any special link between pastor and priest. The teaching would seem to be that the pastoral function was to be exercised as a general responsibility of all believers. There is certainly very slender historical warrant for the present-day notion that the professional healers of disease, whose special concerns seem still to be individual and private rather than public and corporate, have anything to contribute to the understanding of the pastoral role.

Historical speculation apart, there are grounds today for arguing that pastoral functions are in fact exercised to a very considerable extent by men and women who would not be qualified for, or willing to accept, a formal priestly role; and that while it is desirable that ordained men should have pastoral training it is equally desirable that not only should the church recognize explicitly the pastoral functions and responsibilities of certain members of the laity, but also that clergy will benefit greatly if they share a common training with the laity for their pastoral work. The case for this is cogently argued by Dr Michael Wilson in his recent study of the role of the hospital chaplain.[2] The University of Birmingham's Diploma of Pastoral Studies course is specifically offered to laymen as well as clergy.[3]

In any case, the outsider may ask, who wants to be called a sheep? Since the man in the dog-collar professes a pastoral function, does this mean that he alone claims to be properly human, a shepherd, and of a different and superior species to the rest of us? Certainly, the caricaturist has suggested this often enough in an inverted way by portraying the curate as the sheep among men. More seriously, the pastoral model does tend to emphasize the concept of man as a little child of God, weak and dependent, to the virtual exclusion of its necessary counterpart – the concept of the mature man, the son and heir whose task it is to share in the suffering and the hard work of realizing the resurrected body of

Christ. The man who is prepared to consider himself as having come of age needs to be given a job to do.

The experience of the psychiatrist may be relevant here. His major concern is to enable his clients to mature, to behave more responsibly than before. His experience leads him to be wary of attitudes that encourage sheep-like or child-like dependence. Within the psychiatric field, we are currently a good deal pre-occupied with the nature of authority and leadership. Those of us who try to practise a 'therapeutic community' approach[4] run a risk of falling over backwards in our efforts to avoid acting in an authoritarian or controlling way: and we would be as reluctant to think of ourselves as shepherds as we would be to think of our clients as sheep. Even if some of them do display sheep-like characteristics when we first meet them, we have to concentrate our attention on confirming in them their potentiality for growth into mature manhood.

The idea of shepherding raises the difficult problem of leader-ship. I think it is important for pastoral training that it should be continually brought under critical scrutiny, to challenge its uncon-scious implications. Strictly, a leader is someone who knows where to lead. In the context of ministry, this would seem to be a pro-phetic or priestly task rather than a pastoral one. The pastoral task is the care of the flock – looking back at them, making sure they keep together, acting as a focus for them, keeping them from harm. But this distinction of task can rarely be maintained because sheep have a tiresome habit of *following* the shepherd even though he may not have the faintest idea where to go. The modern theorist of management makes the eminently practical observation that the leader in an enterprise has a boundary function[5] – he has to moni-tor the environment and has to see that his flock is so disposed as to be able to act or move appropriately in it. This is a difficult double role and few men are very good at it. I think there are good grounds for giving priority to the leading rather than the caring function whenever there is doubt – so to speak, the priestly or prophetic function should take precedence over the obviously pastoral – because in the long run this is more likely to preserve the flock. For instance, Moses was a great leader, with a clear vision of the direction in which to lead his people, but the record sug-gests that they did not like following him, and I doubt whether the majority of them would have regarded him as a kindly pastor – though in the long run he was of course an effective one.

The tension between leadership and caring functions is apparent in our recent national affairs. Over the last two decades Britain has been preoccupied with welfare provision and the economy. This has been paralleled by a marked diminishment in public concern with the nation's foreign policy, and with a lowering of the status of the foreign minister relative to his cabinet colleagues. The nation seems anxious to be materially healthy, but politicians do not seem able to tell us what we want to be healthy *for*. Until they do, we are likely to go on suffering from a sort of social hypochondriasis.

The implications of this seem to be that it is necessary for the pastor to be constantly alert to the tendency of his flock to acclaim him as leader in situations where his acceptance of the role would involve collusion with them to evade their own proper responsibilities for making decisions; and that it is equally necessary for him not to be seduced into providing pastoral care or counselling for individuals as an easy way out of providing a proper leadership. There are times when involvement in community action is more appropriate, and more costly, than individual counselling.

Let me now turn to another strand of the argument: the tension between care for the individual and care for the flock. There is a tendency for clergy, seeking to improve the quality and effectiveness of their pastoral work, to study the methods of caseworkers and psychotherapists, which have grown up, like curative medicine in general, by intensive study of the individual, isolated from his social context. This has been particularly true in America, and we should be warned by their experience.[6] An English visitor to an American conference of pastoral counsellors wrote to me: 'Some of them have a Christian and theological basis to their work and it arises out of a lively faith. But many are really aggressively secular and see God as existing only within the establishment of good personal relationships. Beyond this he is totally demythologized.' Over the past few years, Dr R. A. Lambourne has spelled out the theological objections to this both in his book *Community, Church and Healing*[7] and in a succession of papers,[8] and has reminded us of the corporate nature of salvation as well as of health. The theological point has been made by others: Suzanne de Dietrich says, 'God does not call isolated individuals, he creates a community.'[9] And Stephen Neill says that 'Man cannot be understood in the isolation of his individual experience'.[10]

The medical profession, of course, has always been aware that one man's illness can affect the health of those near him – notably in the field of infectious disease. But even in the field of preventive medicine it found no need to depart from its individualistic models: it dealt with populations (by methods of random sampling) rather than with communities. It had to wait for the work of Sigmund Freud and his followers before it began to appreciate the vital significance for health of the relationships between people, and thus re-open the way for more corporate models. Even now, such thinking is rare in medical circles and is probably largely confined to social psychiatrists.

This is in spite of empirical observations about the health of communities which have long been known: it is commonly recognized in a military formation, for instance, that high sickness rates are often an index of low morale, and that this can be true whether the diagnoses of individuals' illnesses are of infectious disease, such as malaria, venereal disease or the common cold; or of accidental injuries, or of emotional origin – psychosomatic conditions or neurosis. And it is well recognized by commanders that in the face of high sickness rates, there is an often preferable alternative to multiplying medical services, and that is to take steps to improve morale. These steps are not medical, nor focused on the individual, but consist of measures to improve the quality of leadership, the programme of training and exercise, and the men's awareness of the purposes to which the formation is committed. Morale is a function of the shared sense of security of the men, and of their shared sense of purpose. These two variables are not entirely independent of one another, but both are indispensable. However much care is taken to build up the sense of security, morale will fall unless the men are informed by a common sense of purpose.

This discussion of the morale and health of a corporate body illuminates the proper context in which the individualized care of the single member begins to make theological and practical sense. Whatever individualized care he may receive, the single man will only be able to reach his best possible health, his optimum, inasmuch as he is a participating member of a community or social organism of which the morale is good. Without this context, the best that can be offered him is the mediocre, average condition which medical science so often takes as its norm – the mere absence of disease. And such a condition is of course essentially transient: robbed of his social context and sense of common purpose, it is unlikely that a man will stay free of disease for long. Conversely, of course, morale in the community is likely to be adversely affected if there is frank neglect of the care of the individuals composing it.

It is of the highest importance, therefore, to try to ensure that (in Dr Lambourne's words) 'pastoral training is motivated as much by a struggle for corporate excellence as a struggle against defects'.[11] This is bound to be an uphill task, for the struggle against defects is very seductive. Faced with another human being in distress, the compassionate pastor or doctor is infected with discomfort or anxiety himself, and he tends to erect unconscious defences for self-protection. Two such defences are of great importance. The first is the mental mechanism of projection – of finding some partial or external object at which one can point the finger and say *'that* is the cause of your badness or ill-feeling'. And the natural treatment indicated, of course, is to eradicate *that*. Psychologically, it is irrelevant whether *that* is an evil spirit to be exorcised, a witch to be burned, a tonsil to be taken out or a mosquito to be sprayed with DDT. This is the motivation which is fundamental to scientific medicine as we know it at present. Its analytic method is divisive and atomizing, leading to the reduction of communities into populations and to the separation of the sick man from his social context into an institution – a secular process of ex-communication.

The other defence mechanism I want to mention is that of non-involvement, of detachment. This is preached as a necessary virtue to the doctor and nurse in training: the visual symbol of it is the surgeon's face-mask. However valuable it may be as a safeguard for unprejudiced judgment, it is usually damaging when applied uncritically within an encounter between two human beings. It is essentially depersonalizing, a reduction of the person to a mere assembly of biological part-functions and part-structures. Indeed, this is precisely its value within the scientific/analytic frame of reference. In drawing attention to some of the limitations of scientific method as it bears upon the care of human beings, I would not want to undervalue the achievements of science, of course; but as a psychiatrist, trained to think scientifically, I find that my practice seems to take me into a borderland between science and non-science. I have to beware of over-involvement on the one hand, and over-detachment on the other. I am sure I make as many mistakes through lack of empathy and fellow-feeling with my clients as I do through lack of scientific detachment.

Once we find ourselves acknowledging that a measure of controlled personal involvement is needed in pastoral work we begin to see that the pastor is a participant member of the flock rather than a dispassionate observer of it. He is himself a sheep among other sheep. This is likely to be upsetting to the prejudices of those who have an idea of themselves as shepherds. It means that pastoral training has to concern itself not just with the objective teaching of techniques of counselling or social administration, nor only, indeed, with the objective consideration of the theological question 'What is man?'; but with the far more disturbing questions 'Who am I?'; 'Who do men say that I am?' The training has to stimulate re-consideration of a man's sense of identity.

All of us have to grow up from childhood with remnants at least of the illusion that the universe is centred upon the self – the ego. Even the experience of loving another person, the experience of being part of something wonderful which is bigger than both of us, remains for many people something which can be felt but not effectively thought about or conceptualized – the stuff of poetry rather than reason. So the Christian teaching of losing oneself or dying to save oneself remains for many a mystery or paradox, or else is seen as a call to the total abandonment of that familiar world of which the ego is the experiencing centre. And such a demand, I have no doubt, sends many away sorrowful. But in the light of more corporate concepts of health, we can begin to understand that a man's progress towards maturity of personality involves from his earliest years a recurrent moving outward from the infantile centre of experience: his ego-identity, almost from the moment that he first becomes aware of it, evolves into a shared 'we-identity' – shared with those with whom he chooses to identify – his mother, his parents, his family; and this 'we-identity' is in turn differentiated into ever-enlarging social contexts, of school, occupation, community and nation. Surely, these multiple we-identities wax and wane in importance, and some have to be given up altogether. At times of stress or in ill health, the best of us tend to regress to a simpler sense of personal identity: maturity comes upon us as a tide rolls in from the sea, masked by the continual accession and recession of the waves. But in the light of this we can see how the healthy man is called upon to die a little death repeatedly and continually, to lose each successive self in order that a more mature and comprehensive self may be born. So we discover that the gospel injunction to let the self be lost in order to find the true self is not a sudden, all-or-none commandment so much as a statement of the law of healthy growth of personality.

It is none the less a disturbing experience. Even a little death leaves a sense of loss, a transient vulnerability and sense of doubt. The student needs to find himself in situations where his sense of identity is challenged. In Birmingham, as elsewhere, he finds himself in practical placements where his identity as a minister or student or Christian is not automatically accepted and confirmed by those with whom he works. His supervisor may himself have preconceived ideas of the role of the student in pastoral studies: both student and supervisor may learn about themselves and each other through the breaking of such images. Who do men say that I am? One student, attached to a social worker in a hospital, found himself asked to sit with an unconscious patient with a head injury in an intensive care unit for an hour. What was he supposed to do there? What could his presence *mean*? Psychologically or theologically? He shared his confusion and doubts about himself in this situation in a reflective discussion with other students later, so that all of them, all with their separate ego-identities, were able to share the experience. It is the kind of situation in which nothing can be taught but a great deal can be learned.

Such group reflection upon the role confusion into which pastors inevitably get thrown is an important part of training. It is often an uncomfortable group, full of threats to entrenched ideas and attitudes. The man who conducts it requires some skill in psychodynamics, to ensure as far as possible that participants do not escape the real discomforts of the situation by too ready a retreat behind psychopathological defences, while accepting their doubts and anxieties and yet helping them to confirm one another in a belief in their capacity to grow through suffering them.

Where does all this leave the pastor? He will have had opportunities for making close acquaintance with the techniques, practices and attitudes of the secular caring professions; but he will have had an equally close look at their manifold limitations and shortcomings. He will have lost some of the illusions he may have cherished about their competence and authority, but his own sense of competence and authority will also have taken some knocks. He will probably understand at greater depth what it feels like to be one of society's rejects – chronically sick, or old, or delinquent; he may even have come to identify himself as such a reject at times. Throughout his training, it is important for him – and for the rest of us – that he should have a chance to revise his theology in the light of his secular experience. We badly need more natural theology to help us make sense of present-day society; and since society is undergoing rapid change, natural theology will have to change rapidly too. The old certainties of the faith must be continually reinterpreted if they are to remain relevant. Not every student will find himself able to write a thesis or even a sermon which will do justice to his fresh understanding of the faith. On the Birmingham University course, groups in successive years have been invited to consider the creation of an act of worship to express at the end of the course their common understanding of the faith in the light of their new experience. Their failure to achieve anything which fully satisfies them does not lessen the value of the exercise: perhaps it enhances it.

The pastor has to be ready to stand alongside a man or a woman at the extremities of tension and pain, at times when death is imminent. How can a man be trained to share the experiences of such a person without retreating behind his private defences? Perhaps we have not taken seriously enough the value of a 'wilderness' experience for such training. We are aware that those who have had such an experience, for example, as a prisoner of war, may gain in pastoral ability through having transcended the experience and emotionally digested it; or they may be emotionally crippled by it. But we have not yet contemplated using a controlled experience of this kind for pastoral training. We tend to think of stress in this field in purely psychological terms, of bereavement, for example, or the affirmation of belief among hostile crowds or strangers. But the wilderness experience of which I am thinking is primarily physical, though with psychological results. I contemplate a voluntary course for young healthy men under careful medical supervision, designed to give them an experience of physical exertion, hunger and loneliness, of a degree sufficient to take them a little way past their existing ego-limits, past the limits of their self-control. It would have to be a group exercise: it would lose half its value if the experience were private and unshared. The course would involve a certain length of time in preparatory training for the crucial exercise, and the exercise itself would have to extend over a number of days and nights. I don't know how many, but probably less than the biblical forty. Such training is, I believe, already offered to men in the police and in the armed services: the latter offer what are called 'survival courses'. Participation is voluntary, and I imagine that neither completion of the final exercise, nor any kind of objective criterion of success or failure, are of any significance. It would give a man, once in his life, a chance to become acquainted with the basic limits of his humanity, of what it is like to lose oneself and to be utterly at the mercy of other people. If a theological college were to offer such a course perhaps they would not be overwhelmed with applicants, but the response to a challenge of this kind is unpredictable and it might surprise us.

It may be said that I have given a very cloudy account of what I conceive to be the role of the pastor. Michael Wilson has explored the pastoral role in a particular setting, that of the hospital chaplain. In these words he seems to me to sum up what I feel about the role of the pastor in general:

> The role of the hospital chaplain, like that of his master, is an enigma. Essentially an adventurer, he explores the dangerous territory of man's making and breaking; where every meeting is new and no situation is ever repeated.
>
> He is one who is called to communicate in the language of the other. Quick to turn from work to prayer and prayer to work giving full attention to each: to turn swiftly from weeping with the mother who has lost her baby, to laughing with the mother who is suckling her first born son.
>
> A man for others by calling; formal or informal, authoritative yet servant, powerful yet vulnerable, at the disposal of all but at the mercy of none. At ease with all men and women, young or old, consultant or domestic, because at ease with himself. Friend of all but concerned for the greatest good of each even to wounding. A peace-maker, but not through escape.
>
> In an institution whose tasks include the cure of illness and the care of sick people, he is as interested in the healthy as the sick, and primarily in people who happen to be patients, not patients who happen to be people. He is concerned with health in terms of quality of life not quantity: but is ready to sacrifice his own by giving his life to something more valuable than health. Death for him is not the worst thing that can happen to a man.
>
> But above all he is a man: strong and weak: subject to temptation and doubt, misrepresentation and weariness, as well as joy, hope and encouragement.

He is one of the most public of men, yet his basic work is done in privacy as well as community: he is a man of God, with God and for God, which marks him out as intensely human, able to quicken the humanity of others.[12]

NOTES

1. James Frazer, *The Golden Bough*, abridged ed., Macmillan & Co., 1949, pp.45, 105f.

2. Michael Wilson, *The Hospital – A Place of Truth*, University of Birmingham, 1971, ch. 7 esp., pp.134–36.

3. Report of a Working Party, British Council of Churches, *Pastoral Care and the Training of Ministers*, British Council of Churches and the Institute of Religion and Medicine, n.d., p.77.

4. J. S. Cox, 'Anxiety and Authority in a Therapeutic Community' in *Religion and Medicine*, ed. by M. A. H. Melinsky, SCM Press, 1970, pp.32–78.

5. A. K. Rice, *The Enterprise and its Environment*, Tavistock Publications, 1963, p.15.

6. R. A. Lambourne, 'With Love to the USA' in *Religion and Medicine*, ed. by M. A. H. Melinsky, SCM Press, 1970, pp.132–46.

7. R. A. Lambourne, *Community, Church and Healing*, Darton, Longman & Todd, 1963.

8. R. A. Lambourne, 'Personal Reformation and Political Formation in Pastoral Care', *Journal of Pastoral Care*, vol. 25, no. 3, September 1971; 'Authority and Acceptance in Pastoral Counselling', *Expository Times*, vol. 81, no. 8, May 1970; 'Authority, Personal Knowledge and the Therapeutic Relationship', *Contact*, no. 25, November 1968.

9. S. de Dietrich, *Free Men*, SCM Press, 1961, p.33.

10. S. Niell, *A Genuinely Human Existence*, Constable, 1959, p.36.

11. R. A. Lambourne, 'An Objection to the Proposed National Pastoral Organisation', *Contact*, no. 35, June 1971, p.24.

12. Michael Wilson, op. cit., p.104.

7 Am I my Brother's Keeper?

Ivan D. A. Johnston

Ivan Johnston is Professor of Surgery in the University of Newcastle upon Tyne and Consultant Surgeon to the Royal Victoria Infirmary, Newcastle upon Tyne.

This chapter is based on a paper originally delivered to the Institute's Conference at Bristol in July 1969.

I wish to discuss the dilemmas that have developed in medical science in the field of doctor-patient relationships in the selection of treatment. We shall look at the problems posed by the total and personal responsibility of the doctor for his patient on the one hand, and the immense potential of modern medicine on the other. We shall also examine the conflict that has arisen between the effects and demands of modern care of some patients and the needs of the rest of society. I shall be looking at the subject from a surgical point of view. The activities of surgeons have come under the blaze of modern publicity in recent times and their right to do what they consider best for their patients challenged.

The surgeon is truly his brother's keeper at all times and has been since the days of Hippocrates, who said that 'surgeons had to learn to work with ability, speed and elegance, for the lives of his patients depend on the quality of his craftsmanship', surgeons are naturally anxious to utilize as many of the resources of medical science for their patients as possible. Is this desire always practical?

It would not be amiss to remind ourselves that problems of priorities have existed in the past. The surgeons of the Second World War can recall the agonized discussions which took place as to which casualties should be given some of the precious supplies of penicillin and which did not merit treatment because they had little chance of survival.

The problems loom larger today and differ only in degree. The great expansion of biological knowledge now allows us sometimes to change the course of nature to a remarkable degree. The history of medical science is the story of increasing control over our biological assailants such as infection, neoplasia and, in recent times, tissue rejection. The gains have been very great: tuberculosis is almost conquered, deaths from pneumonia and septicaemia are almost non-existent, and renal transplantation is providing new life for many. The full application of these advances is costly and the problem is really one of priorities for living.

A surgeon has to take decisions on behalf of the desperately ill after weighing up the probability of success, and choose when a hazardous method of treatment should be applied and when it should be withheld. The decisions regarding organ transplantation come into the same category. However, some well-meaning people wish to remove the burden of such decisions from individual doctors and hand them over to some form of committee. There is no evidence from some moves in this direction in other countries that any select committee can ever enhance the quality of a single clinical decision by an experienced doctor.

The experienced and trained medical specialist who knows his patient can handle more data, compute the facts and arrive at a decision more efficiently than any group. He can also apply the golden rule of medical practice – put yourself in your patient's place. This desire to do for the patient what in similar circumstances he would wish done for himself is the patient's best safeguard today. The intimate relationship of doctor and patient must be preserved at all levels of medical practice in spite of the growth of specialization. It has worked well in the past and there is no reason to fear for the future.

I wish now to be more specific and examine some problems of priorities associated with intensive resuscitation, clinical research and the treatment of congenital deformities.

The benefits of intensive care are unequivocal for many, particularly victims of major accidents. By intensive care I mean the specialized nursing, the monitoring of vital functions, the assistance of respiration, the control of cardiac action and the careful attention to the chemical changes in the body which follow injury and coma. Some patients with coronary artery disease and acute respiratory infections also benefit from such intensive care. These methods of treatment are powerful and with their use death can be kept at bay for very long periods of time. The methods, however, must remain the slaves of the physician and not dominate his thinking. The decision whether or not to resuscitate a severely ill patient must be taken by the individual consultant concerned, bearing in mind the nature of underlying diseases and the quality of life to be expected. Age alone is never a basis for the withholding of intensive treatment. Intensive care can be a harrowing experience and it can be misused so that some patients die twice and the dignity of death may be removed. On the other hand, if there is a reasonable chance of worthwhile recovery in any patient, then every effort must be made in resuscitation.

After severe injury, several days of intensive care are often enough to enable evidence to be accumulated that brain damage is probably irreparable. When there is good anatomical and functional evidence of severe brain damage then the surgeon must overcome his reluctance to switch off the machinery which is artificially maintaining life. The prolongation of an artificial existence beyond this point is not in the best interests of any patient or his relatives. Those of us who have seen intensive care staff tackle hopeless odds will be quite certain that none of them would ever terminate a life as long as the faintest hope of recovery remains. This sort of information must reach the public today for their reassurance as they hear of the problems associated with organ donation from dying patients in intensive care units.

Not all intensive care situations end either with complete recovery or with early death. Sometimes we end up, after the withdrawal of all artificial aids, with an unconscious patient living a completely negative existence and the question is raised, when is life no longer human life? Should this sort of basic physiological existence be considered inviolable and accorded human worth? Is personality and the ability to communicate the criteria that should be used in assessing the worth of human life, but who can judge? A mother may see personality in her brain-injured child when everyone else can detect none. When a severely deformed baby is born, or when a burned patient has lost hands, feet and eyes, the clamour is raised that the expected quality of life is too poor to save. However, the range of acceptable quality is great and the potential for recovery often equally great. These considerations must prevent us from laying down any clinical criteria of quality which might lead to ablative steps if the criteria were absent.

The surgeon looking after patients in intensive care units is guided by two ethical principles which are Christian in origin. The first is the sanctity of human life and the second is the compassionate care of the sick. These principles and the Hippocratic promise to help the sick according to ability and judgment do not conflict with the withdrawal of artificial aids to life on occasions. Quality of life is more important than quantity and treatment which ceases to offer quality becomes irrelevant. The withdrawal of such treatment is then logical. In other words, if extraordinary means are used to support a vital function and it later becomes apparent that other hopes and expectations are unfulfilled, then the withdrawal of that treatment is humane.

Some effective forms of modern treatment for a variety of reasons are not always available for patients who could benefit from them. The gap which exists between the ability to treat, for example, renal failure and the availability of artificial kidney machines, highlights this problem.

About 7,000 people continue to die each year in this country from chronic kidney disease. These deaths passed unnoticed ten years ago. Many of these patients are young and only have renal disease, the rest of their body is healthy and about 2,000 of the total are suitable each year for modern treatment with a reasonable chance of success. It costs between £2,000 and £3,000 per year to keep one of these people alive and after ten years the annual bill for treating all those who could benefit would be about £30 million. This is not an impossible sum and would barely buy two modern war-planes. However, such a programme would require about 10,000 skilled personnel to run. The relative lack of medical and ancillary staff is the main reason why a completely adequate renal support programme cannot be organized. Successive governments have failed to provide facilities to train enough personnel to enable the Health Service to keep pace with new methods of treatment which have so much to offer some patients. The inability to provide all that is required is also becoming increasingly evident in many other fields. Public debate and informed opinion is needed to impress upon politicians that medical science really benefits suffering humanity and is not merely a status symbol for hospitals and their staffs.

To return to our theme and the difficult decision as to who should be saved and given a kidney machine with a view to transplantation, clinical considerations must take priority as scanty resources must be used where they are likely to be most effective. The decisions are difficult to make but rarely do we have to consciously choose one patient in preference to another.

Renal transplantation is another aspect of managing these

patients and has its own peculiar problems. A kidney transplant costs about £3,000 and requires the activities of about fifteen to twenty doctors and nurses in an operating theatre for a number of hours as well as a long period of detailed post-operative care. Critics of transplantation programmes have always been able to point out that the amount of money, time and skill required to carry out one successful transplant operation could have been redeployed to relieve a good deal of minor discomforts, such as herniae, and reduce the waiting lists in our hospitals and increase the productivity of the country. My answer to this criticism is simply to ask why should the patient in renal failure be denied treatment, albeit costly, which is capable of restoring him to a useful life? Why should his needs be submerged in deference to the needs of society?

I wish now to turn to the problems raised by clinical research and what is often referred to as experimentation on patients. All doctors vow to consider only treatment which is designed for the benefit of their patients and to abstain from whatever is deleterious or mischievous. All medicine is experimental in one sense. Biological phenomenon do not conform to the law of cause and effect but rather to the more general concept of chance and probability. We do not expect inevitable results when we operate. It is eminently justified to apply a new treatment when all others have failed and the situation demands it so long as evidence is available to show that the new therapy is rational. These decisions are made daily.

However, it is in the field of clinical measurement and physiological observation that the doctor may be accused of not being his brother's keeper. Clearly experiments which are risky or harmful are forbidden. Harmless ones may be permissible and those which have a clear practical application for good are obligatory. For example, it is obligatory that measurements of blood clotting be made in women taking oral contraceptives to find out more about the clotting problems which have caused some deaths recently.

I cannot divert into a discussion as to what constitutes a questionable experiment or what makes an essential investigation. Some would define the daily weighing of patients in hospital as an experiment, while others would consider this a routine procedure not worthy of notice. The rules for clinical investigation are that the patient's informed consent must be obtained and that the procedure be open to the scrutiny of selected colleagues. It is common experience that standards of clinical care increase in an atmosphere of enquiry and investigation. Clinical investigation does not exclude kindly and compassionate care. The investigating physician is his brother's keeper in a very important sense as he must always subordinate his investigation to the individual need of his patient.

Prevention of congenital deformity would be a most attractive solution to one of the problems which faces us today. However, so little is known about the hereditary basis of many malformations that compulsory control of the reproductive life of families already affected is unlikely to be of any value. The frequency of malformations is higher in women approaching the menopause but any attempt to enforce the completion of families by the age of thirty-five would not significantly affect the problem. We are left with a group of unpredictable abnormalities and the earliest period at which the problem can be tackled is clearly after fertilization.

How common are gross deformities today? A detailed survey indicates that the incidence ranges from seventeen to twenty-seven per 1,000 live births. Some of these deformities, such as talipes, polydactly, cleft lip and palate, are not a risk to the life of the child and there is no ethical problem in treatment which invariably improves the situation.

The number of infants surviving with serious cardiac anomalies is increasing and half these children with congenital heart disease are alive at five years. Surgery when it succeeds offers a normal life and removes a disability. The mortality rate although still high is falling and the decision to submit the child to surgery is usually relatively easy as the choice lies between a good chance of normal development and increasing disability and early death. The only problem is one of availability of surgical skills, particularly as an emergency service in the early days of life. Statistics are available indicating the required increase of consultants to improve this service, thus raising again the question of cost in terms of finance and manpower in one more speciality.

I wish now to consider the problems that have arisen with the care of neurological anomalies such as hydrocephalus and spina bifida where early surgical treatment cannot restore all the children involved to a high quality of life. It is in the field of spina bifida that an acute problem in clinical care exists. This deformity occurs in about three per 1,000 live births in this country. Between 2,000 and 3,000 patients survive with this condition each year. This is a relatively recent problem, as formerly ninety per cent of the children died by the end of the first year and the remainder in early childhood. As recently as 1959, no treatment was advised if paralysis was present at birth.

The change in attitude is due to a number of surgical developments such as valves to maintain the ventriculo-atrial shunts and prevent hydrocephalus. Orthopaedic advances, urinary diversion techniques and the control of infection have played a part as well. However, the most important step towards active treatment came from the observation that the extent of limb paralysis and neurological deformity was reduced when closure of the deformity was undertaken as an emergency procedure within hours of birth rather than later following assessment of the situation in terms of the family. This meant, of course, that it was impossible to assess the total potential of the infant in any way before deciding upon surgery and factors which should have been considered were overlooked.

What has been the effect of early surgery to close the defect associated with continuing care? Seventy-five per cent of those operated on survive and fifty per cent are capable of a normal education. It must be remembered that about one third of the survivors have good functional results and one third continue to have a severe paralysis. However, the remainder do live lives of inferior quality and make great demands on educational resources and require many people to look after them.

When a child is born with a large defect three possible lines of action can be taken. First the child may be killed; second no treatment may be given for the defect or any complications and perhaps even feeding reduced and third, the child should be encouraged to live.

I would submit that the deliberate killing of a human being is always wrong and that the refusal to offer available treatment or even food is difficult to justify unless the prognosis is known with reasonable certainty. It remains difficult to decide which of these children should be encouraged to live, but once the decision to treat is taken then we have a responsibility to apply those measures which will give the children the best quality of life.

It has been suggested that paediatric surgeons flushed with the success of early closure of the defects have, by treating all cases, conducted an uncontrolled experiment which has led to a significant number of poor results which thus places an intolerable social and medical burden on the community. It is suggested that the social consequences of early operation should always be considered before any child is accepted for treatment. This view is difficult to condone because it implies that, if the result is going to be poor in terms of mental and physical activity, then for the convenience of the family and the community the child should be destroyed.

It is important that we should look at the problem of after-care carefully to see what is involved medically and socially. The continuing management of the hydrocephalus is a major problem. Eighty per cent of spina bifida babies have a significant degree of hydrocephalus requiring a valve in the first year of life. Revision operations may be required in the first five years and each child may require on the average three more hospital admissions during this time.

Urinary problems are a serious threat. Operations for urinary diversion are becoming more and more necessary and beds will be required for problems of renal failure as well as surgery with its subsequent revision procedures. The number of orthopaedic operations required by a child with spina bifida can be as few as one and as many as sixteen. The mean is around four. About twenty per cent require in-patient treatment to fit braces, splints and instruction in walking. The average stay in hospital for these patients is four months. The extent of the problem is only becoming clear now and it would appear that with a sixty per cent five-year survival, the population of spina bifida children is increasing at the rate of 1,200–1,500 per year in this country. This population has special requirements in much the same way as the renal failure or diabetic population has and these requirements are costly. Every effort must be made to educate the spina bifida child in ordinary schools but a number of residential schools and special day schools will be required. Education is the single most important factor after continuing medical care. These children can contribute to society and the child with a myelomeningocoele has a much greater potential in the community than many other patients with serious defects requiring continuous medical surveillance, but then comparison of worth cannot and should not be a medical decision. The decision will have to be made in the light of the evidence presently being provided and a choice will have to be made between medical care for clearly defined groups such as spina bifida and other social services or amenities. The hospital cost of care for congenital malformities is £4 million per annum (1964 statistics) and the cost to local authorities for mentally defectives is £10 million.

I would like, in conclusion, to look a little into the future which is always a dangerous pastime. How soon will we have to face the ethical problems of the in vitro fertilization of the human ovum? Are we in our permissive society taking one further step towards complete separation of sexual relations and reproduction. It is suggested that the recent work at Cambridge is advancing very rapidly and I think we should ask the question whether experimentation on human living embryos, taking them beyond the two cell stage to growth in the rabbit oviduct, is immoral and whether killing them in such an abnormal situation is also immoral.

Can the clinical aim of attempting to create a pregnancy in women with obliterated Fallopian tubes be enough to justify the present work? Very soon now a decision will have to be taken to permit an artificial embryo to go to term. Will the maturation of such an embryo be normal? Who will bear the responsibility if the initial experiments result in gross foetal abnormalities?

Some biologists have from time to time advocated a future policy of germinal choice in which, for example, germ cell banks would be established containing varieties of semen derived from donors with special characteristics. It is possible that families afflicted with a history of congenital deformity might attempt to avail themselves of such a service arguing from the highest motives. These ideas are not new but they are receiving new attention today as progress is being made on long term hypothermic storage and in vitro fertilization.

At present there are no fully developed techniques for identifying defects at a very early stage of development but it may be that ovum and sperms could be taken from a couple anxious to reproduce but who have had a foetal disaster. After in vitro fertilization of a group of eggs growth would be continued to such a stage that it could be determined which embryos were free from a defect and a satisfactory embryo could be selected for implantation.

We may be gazing into a crystal ball but the day of the genetic manipulator may not be too far off. Medicine is therefore becoming more complicated, more scientific and immensely more effective. The medical team is replacing the old-fashioned personal physician. At the centre of this rapidly changing scene is the patient contributing to further medical knowledge and receiving immense benefit in return.

The ethic of medicine in this country should go a little beyond our title, 'Am I my brother's keeper?', and in many respects fulfil the commandment 'Love thy neighbour as thyself'. This concept of service, responsibility and compassion at a personal level must be guarded jealously by all who are concerned with all aspects of the care of the sick.

8 Decisions – Pastoral and Medical

Michael J. F. Courtenay

Dr Michael Courtenay is a general practitioner who has practised in South London for twenty years. He is particularly interested in marital problems and worked for the Family Planning Association for ten years in this field. He has also been very concerned with the problems of students having worked in the Health Service of the University of Surrey until its move to Guildford.

This chapter is based on a paper read to the 137th Annual Meeting of the British Medical Association at Aberdeen in 1969, being the first time the Institute of Religion and Medicine had been asked to arrange a speaker for the usual gathering of doctors, ministers of religion and members of associated professions before the beginning of the strictly medical programme.

One may well wonder, and in fact it has already been disputed, whether a general practitioner has any *pastoral* function to fulfil. Of course, the term pastoral needs to be defined, but it is noteworthy that those who have criticized the idea in print are hospital-based physicians, and it may be that the dispute rests upon misunderstanding rather than on disagreement. The problem really arises because of different concepts of illness. In the hospital setting illness is of necessity largely seen as pathology more or less divorced from personality. Diseases are diagnosed in patients seen in a setting in which surroundings are made artificially uniform. The whole furnishings of the hospital have nothing to do with the patient who is, moreover, completely detached from his family and normal social environment. The hospital model also pays unconscious lip-service to an out-of-date understanding of observation. Whereas the physical sciences are now well aware that any observing instrument alters the objects observed, there is still the feeling that the hospital doctor can view a patient dispassionately and in a 'scientific' manner in which all personal and social factors can be left to the nurses and the social workers. Strangely enough, this is a travesty of the older discipline of history-taking whose

strength is to bring out every relevant circumstance which may
bear upon the origin of the illness.

In general practice the situation is quite different. The very stuff
of the patients' lives is constantly bearing on the doctor and yet
because, in my generation, our training was firmly hospital based,
the early years in general practice lead either to disillusionment
with general practice or to a gradual awareness that the doctor's
offer of disease-centred medicine is in many cases not meeting the
needs of those in distress. The critics of the pastoral role of the
general practitioner have thought of this need in terms of hospital-
based psychological medicine but this misses the point. It is the
patients' desire to make a *relationship* with the doctor that is at
stake, rather than a more high-powered formal therapeutic situation. It is also clear from studies of patient consultations in general
practice that the general practitioner sees more women than men.
It has often been thought that this was because women of child-
bearing age needed more medical attention because of the higher
morbidity associated with child-bearing and looking after young
children. There may be something in that explanation but according to Parsons and others[1] men look upon medicine more as an
'instrumental' affair and so tend to look towards the hospital,
whereas women need an 'expressive' relationship which necessi-
tates relating in human terms rather than in terms of machinery.
This suggestion is supported by the study of Ann Cartwright[2] on
what patients look for in their general practitioners. It is probably
no accident that the critics of the pastoral role of the general
practitioners are men.

The importance of general practice setting is that the family
doctor himself becomes part of the diagnostic-therapeutic process
by being consulted, or even incorporated into the family, and it is
this function that is common to all the helping professions, who
start out thinking they have a special professional technology to
apply and come up against the hard facts of reality in that it is
often not what is done, but who does it, that matters.

Here is an example to illustrate the practical aspects of the difference between Balint's concept of person-orientated medicine[3]
and disease-orientated medicine. Mr Tudor[4] was a young man
aged twenty-five who came to me complaining of pain in the chest.
He was very worried because a work-mate had had a coronary
thrombosis and he was obviously concerned as to whether he
had the same. The history of the condition did not suggest a

myocardial infarct, and examination showed nothing more than a muscular strain. At that stage, the disease-centred doctor might well have applied 'reassurance'. A little more history taking discovered that the patient was engaged to be married and had sustained the strain in decorating the future home. He was marrying a woman who had already been married and divorced. There was a toddler of the first marriage. Mr Tudor had suddenly been assailed by doubt as to whether he could make his fiancée happy and be a ready-made father to the child, and it is against this context that one might well diagnose 'heartache' of a different, less severe but none-the-less real, condition than that which he had initially feared.

Reassurance then must be a process originating in the patient rather than forced on to him by the doctor. The doctor's technique must therefore be aimed at allowing the patient to come to a fuller understanding of what his symptoms mean, and allow him to come to an independent decision in the light of this increased awareness. As Balint suggests[5]; the feelings of the doctor are a sensitive meter of what the patient is feeling at the time. This meter reading is, however, distorted by what Balint calls the doctor's Apostolic function which represents the sum total of the doctor's expectations of how the patient should behave. It would seem that it is only in this area that the doctor should make decisions, because unless he partly understands his own subconscious reactions to the patients' offers, he will not allow the patient to freely decide what is best in the situation. For instance, in the field of marital difficulties there often arises a situation where the doctor is asked to 'give advice', but if he does so, there is no doubt that he must bear the full responsibility for giving it. Such advice is likely to stem from his apostolic function and must therefore be suspect. However, the appearance of a moral dilemma is often artificial and two examples may illustrate that it may turn out to be a theoretical pitfall rather than a live issue.

Mrs Wallington came complaining of frigidity. She was a woman of twenty-six who had been married some five years. She was a professional worker and so was her husband. She was the only child of rather elderly parents and had been a very shy inhibited girl. Her mother used to insist on dressing her in rather dull clothes right up to the age of eighteen and she had great difficulty in mixing with people and making friends. She joined a church youth club, and there met a man a year or two older who helped her to be more outgoing and independent, and they became engaged and were married. To start with, all went well, but he turned out to be a very careful, obsessional, almost mean individual who suffered from great difficulty in ejaculating during intercourse. The marriage relationship became cooler but in the process Mrs Wallington had matured and was now able to make friends, to go out and mix in the world, and to behave in a normal way socially. At this stage she fell in love with a colleague at work and although she at first recoiled from this she could not give him up, and finally they became lovers. Sexual intercourse was very satisfactory but she was profoundly disturbed and withdrew from the situation and tried to make her marriage work. She became extremely miserable, depressed and frigid, which is when she came for help. The clinical discussions were centred on helping her to understand the pattern of maturation that she had undergone, and she arrived at an agonizing situation, whereby she recognized that she owed her husband a great deal for the help he had given her in coming out of her adolescent shell, and yet realized that their relationship was something of a stepping stone to a more mature relationship with her lover. Her guilt feelings had to be dealt with for a long time and it was only after a further trial of the marriage during which she came to the conclusion that staying with her husband would bring him no happiness either that she finally left him for the other man. Subsequently her husband divorced her, she has married the other man and started a family, having apparently settled down in a stable, warm relationship.

In contrast to this there is the case of Mrs Kingston. She came initially with somatic complaints, namely backache and itching. The latter became chronic and if it had not been for an almost accidental event might have continued so. One day she came saying that her rash had gone and the resolution had followed a particular event, to be described later. She had married a man whom she had pitied because he had been motherless, but had found him dull, uninspiring and she had never achieved an orgasm. They had been friendly with another couple for years and on one particular occasion she had been alone with the man of the other couple and they both suddenly realized they had been in love for some time, intercourse occurred, and she reached orgasm. It was after that that her itchings resolved. However, they told their spouses the situation and it was decided that they should not see each other, and the respective marriages should be maintained.

Mrs Kingston did this for her part ostensibly because she did not want to have a broken home for her son and she was determined that she would keep things as they were, at least until he had grown up. However, soon after this he started truanting from school, became involved with a delinquent gang, was arrested by the police for driving a car without the driver's permission, being also under age, and not insured, and later still has become dependent on drugs.

You will see that the patients made the decisions and the health of the solutions does not seem to be related to any doctrinaire ideas of morality. They might be said to show that it is more important to face the consequences of the lack of a loving relationship honestly than to adhere superficially to moral considerations.

The problem for the doctor can become even more intense when he is dealing with other problems affecting lack of pleasure rather than the relief of pain. It is very often the doctor's own uncertainty as to the rightness of what he is doing that is the main problem. This arises in such situations as when he is asked to give birth control advice to the unmarried. The change from being a reliever of suffering to being a promoter of pleasure may produce guilt feelings in the doctor, because the situation allows of the interpretation that the doctor appears to be encouraging pre-marital intercourse with all its moral overtones. However, if attention is turned away from moral considerations towards understanding each individual request, it soon becomes apparent that, in women anyway, those coming for such contraceptive advice are either in need of help with the process of maturation leading towards marriage, or are suffering from a more vicious type of arrested development which, if not relieved, may well lead to misery and/or promiscuity. It is this situation that opens up a vast field of preventive medicine. For instance, in the case of Miss Knockholt, a girl of nineteen who had had a steady boy friend for a year. She was brought up in a Roman Catholic family, but having fallen in love with a fellow student, they had become lovers. They were both utterly inexperienced and had had some technical sexual difficulty from the start. However, even when this was resolved she still found herself unable to reach orgasm and came complaining of this. In working with her feelings, it rapidly emerged that she had a rather patronizing attitude towards men, which seemed based on her view of the role of her own father in the family. He was seen as a weak and pitiable individual and it was something of this feel-

ing that was carried over to her fiancé, and which prevented her
from being able to appreciate what he gave her in love-making.
With the case of Mrs Kingston in mind, it would seem that it
might well be better medical practice to deal with the problem pre-
maritally than to leave it until a child might be involved.

Another difficult situation arises when there is a request for an
abortion. In spite of recent legislation, the medical indications for
termination of pregnancy still seem to be obscure if they are considered in relation to fixed principles. Even when the problem is
looked at on an individual basis, great difficulty in arriving at the
right conclusion may be experienced. Very often the outright
request for what is a self-prescribed form of treatment arouses
hostility in the doctor, who likes to be thought of as someone
whose opinion is sought rather than somebody who is told what to
do. In spite of these resistances it is remarkable how some women
are so determined that the pregnancy should be terminated that
they will pursue their aim by one means or another until it is
achieved. The situation may be illustrated by two examples.

Miss Dollis, a girl of twenty, became pregnant by her boy friend
who felt unable at first to take on the responsibilities of marriage
and fatherhood, and she obtained an abortion. Less than a year
later she presented pregnant once more and at a stage when
termination would have been difficult technically. In talking to her
it was clear that she had really wanted to have the first baby, and
it was only because the boy friend did not seem mature enough to
be a father that she had engineered the abortion. Although the
boy friend was still hesitant, it was quite clear that she desperately
wanted to have his child and in helping both of them to understand their anxieties and aspirations throughout the remainder of
the pregnancy, their original intention to have the child adopted
was finally reversed and they decided to marry and keep the child.

On the other hand when Miss Grangewood became pregnant,
she was very unsure of what she really wanted. She felt confused
and unable to come to any decision. Her boy friend definitely
did not want to take the responsibility of the child and this was
the factor that finally made her seek an abortion. When it was
over she felt a great sense of loss and in consequence became very
angry with the man whom she threw over. In spite of this she
remained tense, irritable and had difficulty in concentrating on
her work for a whole year, and it was in this situation that she
sought medical advice. In going into the matter it emerged that

she had remained in the same ambivalent state as she had experienced before the abortion. On the one hand, there were strong maternal urges, and on the other a feeling that she wished to complete her professional training and be intellectually independent. It seemed that it was the conflict between these two aspects of her feelings that produced her inability to decide about the abortion initially, as well as her anxiety symptoms. Subsequently, she became aware that her anger at the boy friend was largely a projection of her own anger against the unmaternal part of herself and it was only with this understanding that she was able to resolve the immediate conflict, though not without suffering a period of intense mourning for her aborted baby.

It would seem that the feelings necessary to allow the happy continuation of a pregnancy somehow depend on a degree of emotional maturity beyond the stage where a merely sexual relationship can be satisfactorily maintained. A woman has to feel ready to become a mother even though sexual and maternal feelings are reasonably well developed, and if there are unconscious factors militating against this ripeness, a request for an abortion is likely.

While such opportunities for preventive medicine with patients before their marriage occur fairly frequently, there is no doubt that doctor-patient contacts of this nature tend to be haphazard affairs. There are other more firmly structured contacts in general practice which also have great potential for increasing understanding. In the 'well-baby' clinic there is a vast, almost untapped, field of preventive medicine. It is common place that babies feeding difficulties and disturbed sleep are often the result of maternal anxiety. The danger here is to apply doctor-centred reassurance without a full understanding of the process leading to the anxiety. This is all the more a pity because in such a setting the doctor has the opportunity to help not only the mother and the child, but indirectly, the husband and any other children. If the mother has doubts about her maternal capacity she may also have doubts about her femininity, and this may spill over into marital disharmony as well as spreading the contagion to the next generation by depriving them of affection. It is therefore essential to explore the root causes of the problems and allow the mothers to see the problem as it is, rather than papering over the cracks with gripe water and chloral.

Take the case of Mrs Stanford who was convinced that her baby was not taking sufficient nourishment. It was obvious that as he was gaining weight steadily this was a feeling of not giving enough to the baby rather than a fact. Looking into what the feeling meant uncovered an unhappy sexual relationship in the marriage and a behaviour disorder in the baby's elder sister. It was only in dealing with the overall dynamics of the family situation that allowed Mrs Stanford to feel a competent mother and a contented wife, and by then her worry over the baby's nutrition had vanished.

Lastly, we must return to the doctor himself. He always finds it difficult to forgive the patient who will not get better. This need to feel omnipotent is perhaps the curse of our profession. The patient with bulky case notes is a constant reminder of our failure, but the nature of our failing may be that we have directed all our attention on decisions about morbidity rather than getting in touch with the patient's own internal indecision. It should not be forgotten that Balint has shown that some patients seem to need a 'bad' doctor.[6] Perhaps the greatest remedy for our failing is the care of the dying patient and here too we may learn from the technique of our colleagues of previous generations who felt that holding the patient's hands was as important as giving opiates. It is perhaps because of the great increase in our capacity for treatment that leads us towards the hubris of thinking that we should be able to stay the Reaper's hand for ever. It was only the courage of one patient dying of neoplastic disease who gently led me to help her discover the truth about her illness, that showed me that a sincere relationship between doctor and patient can transform the management of a terminal illness from a miserable business into a positive experience for both doctor and patient.

In caring for Mrs Walton in her last illness the doctor had to squarely face the fact that cure was virtually out of the question, but with encouragement from her, explored her anxieties as they arose so that the threat to his therapeutic potency dissolved into a new doctor-patient relationship. Because the doctor no longer felt threatened, he was able to identify himself with her and so help by gradually admitting a weakness in the situation parallel to hers. This dissipated the loneliness of her position in a way analogous to the situation in the treatment of a depression, in which the therapist has first to meet the patient in the slough of despond before they both can climb out of it together. Although this might be thought to be a false analogy in that the patient dies while leaving the doctor to continue living; those who have had a similar experience may be able to agree with me that life is essentially a quality rather than a quantity, and that the *internal world* may often be more important than the external. Thus it is the making of internal decisions in both patient and doctor which is of paramount importance. Action based on external appearances is often easy and equally often inept, while the internal situation may belie appearances, as Stendhal[7] keenly appreciated with his artistic insight in the Charterhouse of Parma, when Fabrizio is imprisoned in the Farnese tower, but completely happy because of his closeness to Clelia, while his friends in the city believe him to be overwhelmed by the deepest despair.

If the doctor's pastoral understanding is at fault, his medical decisions may be irrelevant.

NOTES

1. J. Parsons and others, *Family Socialization and Interaction Process*, Glencoe, Illinois: The Free Press, 1955.

2. Ann Cartwright, *The Patients and Their Doctor*, Routledge, Kegan & Paul, 1967.

3. M. Balint, 'The Structure of the Training-cum-Research Seminars', *The Journal of the Royal College General Practitioners*, vol. 17, No. 81, April 1969.

4. In this chapter all the patients' names have been changed and the material disguised.

5. M. and E. Balint, *Psychotherapeutic Techniques in Medicine*, Tavistock Publications, 1961, p.71.

6. M. Balint, *The Doctor, his Patient and the Illness*, 2nd ed., Pitman Medical, 1964, pp.233ff.

7. Stendhal, *The Charterhouse of Parma*, Penguin Classics, 1958, pp.318ff.

9   The Abortion Decision

David W. Millard

David Millard qualified in medicine at the University of Birmingham. After military service he was trained as a psychiatrist and was for some years a consultant at a Birmingham psychiatric hospital. He is now teaching social workers as Lecturer in Applied Social Studies in the University of Oxford, and is an honorary consultant psychiatrist to the Isis Hospitals Group.

This chapter is based largely upon a consultation held under the aegis of the Birmingham Group of the IRM in February 1970. The chairman was Mr Wilfrid Mills, F.R.C.O.G. Case histories were presented by Miss Victoria Currie, Mrs Sheila Noble and Mrs Joyce Cummins, and a philosophical analysis by the Rev. D. W. Hardy, Lecturer in Modern Theological Thought, University of Birmingham. It first appeared as an article in the *British Journal of Social Work* I, 2, and permission to reprint is gratefully acknowledged.

Introduction

The Abortion Act 1967 came into force on 27 April 1968. Of the 65,241 abortions carried out during the first eighteen months of the operation of the Act and analysed by Diggory, Peel and Potts[1] some seventy two per cent were performed upon the grounds 'that the continuance of the pregnancy would involve ... injury to the physical or mental health of the pregnant woman ... greater than if the pregnancy were terminated'.[2] The Act also permits risk to the physical or mental health of existing children in her family to be considered, and a further twenty per cent of notified abortions are carried out on these grounds. It allows the woman's (but nobody else's) 'actual or reasonably foreseeable environment' to be taken into account in reaching a decision.

These are the clauses covering the psychological and social indications for therapeutic abortion. Such problems constitute the vast majority among cases where the question of termination arises; they also present the greatest opportunity for divergence of professional judgment and for consequent variation in practice. Situations in which the advice given to a patient or client is largely dependent upon the subjective assessment of a complex of factors are, of course, commonplace in medical and social-work experience. Generally, the person offering the advice is guided by an inner, rather ill-formulated, awareness of the professional consensus as to what constitutes a reasonable course of action in a particular situation. Such a consensus could hardly be said to exist in this field at present. Its lack underlies widespread anxiety concerning the workings of the Act. This is manifest in the Inquiry by the Royal College of Obstetricians and Gynaecologists into the first year's operation of the Act.[3] Sixty per cent of the gynaecologists who responded to this Inquiry considered that the terms of the Act should be made more restrictive (mainly by removing the so-called 'social' clauses), but they add: 'The great majority... emphasised that the real problem is not the wording of the Abortion Act but its interpretation.' A similar view appears to have been taken by the Department of Health and Social Security in setting up the committee of enquiry under the chairmanship of Mrs Justice Lane.[4]

The final responsibility for making the operation lawful rests with 'two medical practitioners' who are required to reach an 'opinion, formed in good faith'.[5] In many cases, however, the doctors are glad to depend upon the help of colleagues in other disciplines in forming their opinion – see, for instance, Oates[6] – and the range of possible contributors to the decision is, in fact, rather wide.

It seems important to base a discussion of the complexities of the decision process in these situations upon actual case material, and this paper therefore presents extended accounts of three patients. These are preceded by a brief discussion of aspects of the psychology of decision-making and followed by an analysis of various factors involved in coming to a decision.

Psychological Considerations

The contributions of scientific psychology to understanding the decision process are relatively few, rather scattered in the literature, and remote from real-life situations. Material up to 1955 was collected by Johnson,[7] upon whose summary the following reflections are based. Psychologists would characteristically consider the properties of three separate elements in the situation, namely, (1) the *stimulus material* (i.e. the clinical and social data brought by the patient), (2) the *person making the judgment* and (3) the *response* (i.e. the form which the decision takes).

1. *Stimulus material.* Many of the empirical investigations of decision-making are concerned with relatively simple situations. However, several studies attest the obvious points that judgments of abstract characteristics, such as we are concerned with, are difficult, and that difficult decisions are associated with an increased number of errors, a greater length of time required to reach a conclusion and a reduction in certainty of the conclusion. In such studies, it is commonly found that judgments are influenced by various features of the stimulus material other than those immediately apparent, and that the judges are sometimes not consciously aware of this fact. This perhaps corresponds to the desirable quality of sensitivity, or breadth of awareness, in the clinician or caseworker. Where a judgment of some important aspect of the material is impossible, it is often found that rather than refrain from offering an opinion on the matter, the judge will base a decision on some other aspect of the stimulus and that such judgments are likely to be affectively toned. Johnson comments 'This phenomenon is regularly observed in judgment of the controversial issues of the day, because they are abstract and difficult, and the content is usually of affective significance'[8] – surely a remark of direct application to discussions of abortion. Finally, judgments can in principle be improved, and such improvement comes about largely through identifying the important aspects of the stimulus material and ascribing a measure of importance ('weighting') to each. This paper begins to attempt this in terms of the three case histories presented. Agreement between judges appears to be closer where it is based upon an analysis into the component parts of a complex situation rather than an 'holistic' assessment – at least in one investigation (in a quite unrelated field) in which the two approaches could be compared experimentally.[9]

2. *The judges.* In several investigations it has been found that persons making difficult judgments give extra weight to the views of those whom (whether appropriately or not) they regard as expert, and to those views attributed (rightly or wrongly) to the majority of a group with whom they identify. This is, of course, a psychological formulation of the process of developing a professional consensus and, incidentally, an encouragement to the publication of case material.

3. *The response.* In many of the studies summarized by Johnson, the nature of the response has been specified by the investigator. In the present case, however, there are some particular difficulties. These arise because there appears to be a transition in the reasoning process used. The *final* question to be answered is whether to terminate the pregnancy or not – a simple alternative, admitting of no middle way. Following William James, we may call this a 'tough-minded' decision.

It is reached, however, by means of a series of *prior* questions of a different sort, involving 'tender-minded' decisions; questions, that is, to which there are scarcely any unequivocal answers. These are questions of degree – e.g. the *extent* of the woman's depression or of the adversity of her housing conditions or of the psychopathy of her husband – the answers to which do not fall into discrete categories but are distributed along some imagined scale. This situation is entirely familiar to social workers and psychiatrists, such matters are part of their professional stereotype. And where the answer to a 'tender-minded' question turns out to have been mistaken, it tends not to have been *completely* wrong and grounds can usually be found (satisfying to the worker, at any rate) for excusing and explaining the situation. It may be, however, that the professional stereotype of the gynaecologist is much more to concern himself with 'tough-minded' questions – his actions tend to be irrevocable.

Illustrative Case Histories

Case I. An application for termination of pregnancy accepted: absence of a stable marital relationship

A thirty-six-year-old married woman attended an ante-natal clinic at the eleventh week of her third pregnancy and asked for termination. She was referred first to a medical social worker and subsequently to a psychiatrist.

She was one of two sisters, the other being happily married with several children. Her father was described as a distant, Victorian figure with a great need to dominate the home. He was a rigid, church-going man 'who does not practise what he preaches' and her relationship with him was so bad that during her second pregnancy she was not on speaking terms with him although living in the same house. Her mother, aged forty when the patient was born, was a weak person, dominated and frightened by the patient's father. Life in the parental home, where she had continued to live to the age of thirty, offered her very little support and was characterized by considerable friction. At this time she left her home and the stable job in which she had spent sixteen years, and had a considerable variety of occupations.

Two years later she had her first pregnancy and was referred to a medical social worker in the last month for help in arranging an adoption. The putative father was a casual acquaintance at a holiday camp and although he had made a half-hearted proposal, they both felt marriage was not the answer and he had given her some money and gone overseas. She discussed him with remarkably little show of feeling. She felt inadequate and bad because of society's attitude towards unmarried mothers.

Following her normal confinement she was allowed not to have to look after the child while in the hospital (adoption being planned) but she was observed to make frequent trips to the nursery to look at him. She had been very particular in her choice of foster-home for the child and had rejected several possibilities. When they were discharged from hospital she insisted on taking the child to the foster parents herself. One month later she removed the child and returned with him to the parental home. She made no reply to a letter from the social worker offering to see her again.

Twenty months later she returned with a second pregnancy, twenty-two weeks advanced. She was still unmarried and was again living with her parents, although the friction between them was very great. Her son, then aged twenty months – described by the social worker as a 'lively, attractive and intelligent little boy' – was being looked after while she was out at work, by her seventy-six-year-old mother. At the clinic he seemed demanding of mother's time and attention, but she was concerned about him. Termination of the pregnancy was not considered, but she was referred at this earlier stage to the social worker. Again she expressed little feeling for the putative father who was a married man with several children. He had talked vaguely about divorce but they drifted apart and she saw very little of him during the pregnancy. After another normal confinement she looked after her child, but with a good deal of anxiety and there were considerable feeding difficulties. The child was discharged to foster parents and, despite strongly ambivalent feelings on the patient's part, was later adopted. Contact between the patient and the hospital social work department was again lost.

She reappeared with a third pregnancy some eighteen months later and requested termination. By this time she had been married for four months. Her husband was a widower with two older children. She said she felt she had been rushed into marriage and had become pregnant before she had had time to adjust herself to her new situation. Her parents were not in favour of the marriage and she herself had come to regret it bitterly. She complained of her husband's aggressive attitude, and she had left him two weeks previously to return to her parents. When he first heard of her pregnancy her husband had offered to 'get rid of it' for her, but she was scandalized by this and refused.

She was in a very distressed state and said she could not possibly go back to her husband. Her parents found her son's behaviour almost too much to put up with and certainly would not tolerate another child in the house. Also she doubted whether she herself could manage another child.

The social worker eventually decided not to recommend that this pregnancy be terminated. Some of her reasons were that the patient was expressing feelings of being a bad person and a failure, that the adoption of the second child had been very traumatic and she wondered if a termination would have serious side-effects, and that the patient was feeling very isolated and unloved. However, a psychiatrist, to whom the patient was then referred, took the other view. He did not recommend this on psychiatric grounds, but on social grounds. He felt that she was '... so unsuccessful in the management of her affairs that if she went on to have this child her own well-being and more importantly that of her son would be severely compromised'. The gynaecologist preferred the psychiatrist's advice and an abortion was carried out. She was also sterilized.

Case II. An application for termination of pregnancy accepted: stable marital relationship; follow-up

A twenty-four-year-old married woman was referred when about two months advanced in her fifth pregnancy, the second child having died of cerebral haemorrhage when six hours old. Her remaining three children were aged between three and half years and seven months. She had recently been fitted with an inter-uterine coil, but this had failed. She had found it difficult to cope; she did

not really want an abortion but felt that she must have one. She was
a Roman Catholic and had been married for four and a half years.
The gynaecologist referred her for the social worker's opinion concerning her 'ultimate feelings' about termination.

She had formerly been employed as a bookbinder, her husband
aged twenty-seven being a printer who was under treatment by
his general practitioner for spondylitis. Her husband's parents
lived nearby, her mother had died three years previously from
cancer, but her father was still alive and she had an older married
sister.

Her parents had been well disposed towards her and the early
years of her marriage were comparatively easy. The unexpected
death of their second child only six hours after a home confinement in the absence of doctor or midwife had been a great shock
but they had faced it as well as they could. The next child, born
one year later, was looked on as a kind of compensation. The
youngest child had been unplanned and her husband was said to
have been using a sheath at the time; the present pregnancy was
also unplanned and she was desperately concerned that she could
not look after four children under the age of five. She said she was
depressed, often unreasonably angry with the children, and she
feared she might have a mental breakdown. The social worker
felt that when not under stress she was a gentle and understanding
mother, with good relationships to husband and children.

The husband's job was secure but with little prospect of expand-
ing his earnings of £19 weekly. Their expenses included mortgage
repayments of £4 per week.

She had been advised against using oral contraception because
of a tendency to varicose veins, but she and her husband were
agreed on the desirability of sterilization.

The social worker felt that the patient had reservations about
termination because she felt it was an extreme measure, and she
was influenced by her early upbringing as a Roman Catholic. Her
own father was Roman Catholic but her husband's parents had
reservations about her marriage as they are Church of England.
The husband was concerned for his wife, on the grounds that she
might suddenly break down, and also about his own earning ability
which he thought might fluctuate because of his spinal trouble.
He felt he could not support another child even supposing his
wife could manage. He could sympathize with his wife's misgivings
but in his view the termination of this pregnancy would help the

upbringing of the other children. The social worker considered she was a thoughtful person (e.g. they openly discussed the possibility of depression resulting from mourning after a termination) who would have no more regrets over terminating this pregnancy than if she had kept it and was obliged to struggle on in more attenuated circumstances, and an abortion was therefore advised.

Follow up. Two days after the operation she was saying she must put everything connected with abortion out of her mind. When it was suggested that this might be unwise, she said she thought she might be able to talk about it with her husband. She agreed that no course of action open to her would have been entirely free of anxiety, and that she had been already near breaking point. She had nonetheless been very involved with this child. Next day the ward staff reported she was better.

Four days later she was more cheerful – partly because the other children had visited her in hospital over the week-end. She felt they had grown up while she had been in hospital and she felt the need to return home to be with them. The husband had looked after them in her absence and intended to use a week of his holiday to be at home with her.

She then disclosed that before she came into hospital her father had been to see her and said very explicitly that on the basis of his own religious position he did not think it was right for her to go forward for termination and she was distressed because she had by then made up her own mind. Her sister had perhaps influenced him but she was better off and had contrived to produce her own children at two-yearly intervals! There was some real jealousy between the sisters. The sister had also travelled from the north of England to try to dissuade her, and when she failed she had condemned her. The social worker suggested that this was a decision for her, and the patient agreed adding that family relations might be less difficult in the future because her sister was shortly going to emigrate. She felt the decision had been the right one for her and for the children, and she was anxious to go home. On the day of her discharge she was quite composed and agreed to further contact with the social worker (which would not normally have been arranged but for the purpose of collecting the following information).

In a subsequent letter she said she was feeling fine and had been coping with the children and housework although when she had first come out of hospital she had not found things as easy as she thought they would be. She was a bit depressed the first couple of weeks. The operation had been on her mind a lot at first and she wondered if she had done the right thing and felt very ashamed at herself for agreeing to such an awful thing. Later she realized she could not remember what she had felt like before the operation; she had forgotten how bad things were and so could not decide whether it was right or wrong. Her husband was quite convinced it was for her good. She thought in time she would feel that the operation was right, meanwhile she was looking forward to the approach of Christmas and the New Year.

Later the social worker made a home visit. The patient had been fairly well in herself, and on her return home had been encouraged by the reassurance of her children. Their needs had helped to divert her mind from her loss. When things were easy she most missed the lost child and thought she might perhaps have managed after all. She did not feel robbed of anything, but a 'void' in the sense of losing a child whom she could know and recognize as her own. The baby had been very real to her and she was involved in its life and its survival. She had these feelings at times of depression. She felt she might continue to feel like this for a few more months, until the date at which the child would have been born. She was mourning a loss she could not believe would be filled by the other children. But she could not believe it had been done in the best interests of her children and that indirectly it helped her husband. She was quiet and without reproach. Her husband thought that she had been occasionally depressed but had not shown nearly as much distress as when she had been pregnant, and even before then when the children were younger and more dependent. The social worker thought that he carried a fair share of his responsibilities in caring for his children. The husband's parents provided intermittent help, the patient's sister left England unregretted, but her father kept in touch and visited frequently. He had not approached her about the operation since she had left the hospital. They had made friends with some neighbours who acted as baby-sitters and they had been able to go out together on a few occasions for the first time in their marriage.

The general practitioner thought that she was a good mother who had been through a very bad time when her second child died. He was certain the subsequent children had replaced this child for her, but he thought that she was strongly influenced by her early religious upbringing. She was not divided within herself about the termination but 'thought she must have done something wrong for this to have happened to her'. He himself had no doubts about the rightness of her termination. She was very distressed when she found herself pregnant and this was in addition to her normal state of anxiety.

Case III. An application for termination of pregnancy refused; illustrating the need for after-care

This family presented through a Child Guidance Clinic to which the second of the five children was referred with school phobia. The social worker retained contact with them for two and a half years.

The husband had worked as a polisher, earning about £25 weekly, until six years before the referral. Since then he had not worked but had suffered from a stomach ulcer, for which he had been operated upon, spinal trouble, also treated surgically, and depression for which he had spent three months in hospital. He still had feelings of hopelessness and thoughts of dying.

The patient had been a timid child, her father had died when she was twelve years old and she was distressed by her mother's re-marriage two years later. She felt 'emotionally abandoned', and went to live with a married sister. She described herself as 'soft', and said she would do anything to avoid a row. When seen with her daughter at the Clinic she was anxious and agitated and com-plaining of her difficulty in controlling the children. She would threaten to have them put away until their father was better.

At the second interview, she was very distressed because she thought she was pregnant. Her last child had been unwanted and she had asked her general practitioner for a termination but he had not wanted this. He had suggested oral contraception but she had thought it would make her ill and her husband had also strongly objected so she had not taken the tablets. With the social worker's encouragement she again approached her general prac-titioner to discuss the possibility of an abortion, but she said he was very angry because she had not taken his contraceptive advice and he had told her off for asking for a termination, as she was a healthy woman.

Throughout her pregnancy, the patient attended the Child Guid-ance Clinic with her daughter (whose school phobia improved) and the social worker visited at home. She remained depressed and terrified of the confinement – as she had been on each previous occasion. In the final three weeks she lost 13 lbs. in weight and became very afraid that she would die and leave the care of her large family to her sick husband.

Follow-up. Two months after the confinement the health visitor telephoned to express concern at the patient's mental state and the social worker visited again. She was crying all day and had become very obese. Her husband confirmed that she was unable to cope with the new baby and with household jobs although he gave her all the help he could.

Because of the patient's poor relationship with the general practitioner the social worker contacted him on her behalf and found him helpful. He prescribed an anti-depressant but the patient did not stick to the tablets because of side effects and she was subsequently unwilling to see him again.

In the search for other ways of helping his patient, it was arranged for her to be seen by the domiciliary Family Planning Association service to be fitted with an inter-uterine contraceptive, but when the doctor arrived at the house the husband was abusive and would not agree to the procedure. Later casework with the family made clear the husband's need to dominate, his fantasies that his wife would be promiscuous if contraception were used, and his fears that oral contraception could make a woman more sexually demanding and hence add to his own feelings of inadequacy. These ideas were worked through and he ultimately agreed to his wife being fitted. She later said that he still accused her of looking at other men but she felt strong enough not to be distressed by this.

However, she remained for a time depressed and agitated and, largely, housebound. She expressed fears for her own and her children's death, and that her own aggression would harm the baby (although all the children were well cared for physically). She was eventually prescribed further anti-depressants by the Child Guidance Clinic psychiatrist to which she responded satisfactorily and the complex problems of the family were gradually resolved.

Discussion of Cases

Using the sub-divisions already employed in the psychological discussion, we now consider some aspects of the case material –

the stimulus to decision-making. Subsequently we discuss the participants in the decision, the social context of the decision, and the nature of the judgments made.

It is not the purpose of this paper to list comprehensively the social and psychological indications for terminating pregnancies. Rather it is to draw out of the case illustrations of the features that seem to weight the decision.

In Case I the reasons for performing the abortion seem to have been chiefly that the family environment into which the child would have to be born was already beset with severe interpersonal problems, that the mother was materially without the support of her husband (whose explicit agreement to the procedure was apparently not sought – presumably because he was held by his own behaviour to have put himself out of communication with the patient–helper system) and that she would be unlikely to be able to detach herself from this pathological environment in the foreseeable future. The interaction between the patient and her parents, and their personal needs, seem to have been important in the decision. However, the Abortion Act specifically permits injury to the health only of existing children, and of no other members of the family, to be taken into account. The extent to which rejected pregnancies are considered as manifestations of family pathology is unknown, but where this view is taken, some rationalization may be required to bring the decision within the law.

The degree of emotional distress present in this patient was not held sufficient to justify termination on psychiatric grounds.

In Case II the relevant factors appear to have been the patient's state of reactive depression and anxiety, her husband's illness and the consequent restriction on his earning capacity, the presence of three healthily-developing children, possibly the factor of failed contraception, and (very importantly) the impression that she would use the experience of the abortion in a healthy fashion. The last-mentioned factor receives further discussion later. It is related, however, to the absence of serious problems in her premarital personality and relationships, her stable home and supportive husband (in contrast to Case I).

Case III differs in that the request for termination was rejected. In comparison with Cases I and II, however, the extent of the patient's depression is much greater (indeed there is some doubt as to whether the condition in Case II could be designated a depressive illness – the expressed guilt may well have been induced by the circumstances of the case rather than being in any real sense innate. Even doubt exists in regard to Case I). In Case II, also, the family relationships, and perhaps the material circumstances, appear to have been a good deal more adverse than in Case I, and, like Case II, there was the factor of unsuccessful contraception. The latter factor, however, differs between the two patients in that in Case III she was held morally culpable for this failure whereas in Case II this was not so. Case III also illustrates that it may also be possible to bring a successful outcome to many cases whatever the decision, given adequate resources. It is perhaps fortunate that this particular family happened to be in touch with an agency able to provide for them.

The variability in the stimulus material and in its interpretation is well illustrated. How might some order be brought into this complexity? The material presented does not allow of a critical working-out of this problem, but it is suggested that one approach might be to devise a hierarchy of preferred reasons for advising termination. To some extent the Act provides this, in that risk to life of the pregnant woman precedes concern for existing children and that intrinsic personal features precede environmental. However, the Act itself is not comprehensive in this respect. Among psychiatric disorders, the acceptance of a particular situation as constituting a valid indication for therapeutic abortion would probably be given most strongly to illness of organic aetiology, followed, in order, by psychoses, neurosis and personality disorder. Social factors would rank lower than psychological, which are themselves below physical factors. The lower in the hierarchy a particular form of disability is placed, the more severe needs to be its deviation from the normal range for it to count. However, as will appear later, it might well be that judges from different professional backgrounds would arrange the various possible factors in quite different hierarchical orders, and a problem requiring resolution between the professions concerned would thus be defined.

The Participants in the Decision

It is clear that a considerable number of individuals may contribute in one way or another to the decision.

1. *The patient.* She herself is obviously an important actor in the decision-making process. She brings her accustomed style of life, with its complex of responsibilities and expectations. She also brings into the situation the foetus, and the foetus is a focus for

her anxieties regarding her style of life. It is for her a 'material symbol', i.e. not only does it symbolize a potential disruption of the pattern of her life, but it is the immediate cause of it. In one sense, the foetus may be an opponent of the mother, and a comparatively weak one (so that we have little difficulty in accepting a reductive, dehumanizing view like non-viability before twenty-eight weeks). In wanting to be rid of the foetus she wants to be rid of the threat to her life style.

The patient may have secretly determined that she will have an abortion and her request for advice, or for a doctor to consider the matter, may be merely a public statement of this decision. On the other hand, she may be genuinely uncertain as to what she wishes will happen, and be in need of guidance. Occasionally her request may be an attempt to obtain the doctor's support – perhaps against another member of her own family – in *not* having an abortion.

The possibilities raise questions concerning responsibility and power. What is a responsible decision? What is the place of authority – or power – in the process of reaching a decision? Does the rejection of the principle of 'abortion on request' sometimes deny to the patient her proper degree of responsibility in reaching the appropriate decision? In situations where 'abortion on request' is obtainable, *de facto* if not *de jure*, is the woman forced to accept a degree of responsibility which is inappropriate?

2. *The patient's family.* Family processes are evident in all the Cases considered. The idea of termination may well have been put into the patient's mind by her husband (Case I), or her conceiving of the idea may have been encouraged, or 'authorized', by him (or, in other cases, by a boy-friend, parent, confidant, or other significant person). Determinants of the final decision of this kind arise right outside the hospital situation, and are sometimes unrecognized. The gap between what is necessary from the perspective of the outside world and what is possible within the hospital may well seem unbridgeable. Yet if no attempt is made to bridge it, is not the doctor handing over some of his power to entirely unknown influences? On the other hand, an undue emphasis on family collusion should not allow the wife to opt out of her proper role in the decision-making process.

3. *The general practitioner.* He may be better placed to know about the family processes behind a request for termination of pregnancy, or his knowledge may be deficient. In any case his values will influence his judgment. A little is known of the atti-

tudes of the general practitioners in the case discussed. In Case I
he made no direct request for termination but simply asked for
the consultant's '. . . opinion concerning this pregnancy', but he
began his referral letter with the value-laden remark: 'This unfortunate girl appears to have no discrimination in the men she
chooses.'

General practitioners, however, have a good deal of discrimination in the gynaecologists they choose. Where, as is inevitable,
gynaecologists vary in the attitude towards therapeutic abortion
this is a choice which may clearly influence the way the final
decision goes.

In Case II it was known that the general practitioner had no
doubts about the rightness of the patient's termination. In Case III
the patient is said to have told the social worker that her general
practitioner had angrily refused to refer her for consideration for
termination because she had not been able to follow his earlier
advice to adopt contraceptive measures. There appeared, however,
to be compelling reasons in the family psychopathology why contraception would have been difficult for them to accept. This case
demonstrates clearly the power of the doctor in some situations –
if only to veto further discussion.

4. *The gynaecologist*. It would be possible to take the view (e.g.
in Case II) that the patient appeared to have been left feeling that
the decision and its accompanying guilt had been hers whereas she
should have been able to feel that the decision was a medical one
and that she was merely following the more dispassionate advice of
the doctors. (The question whether a patient should necessarily be
saved from the doubt and uncertainty that accompanies a choice
of this kind is itself of interest and will be considered later.) Two
alternative approaches exist in attempting to relieve this burden:
(i) a quick decision, made on the day of the patient's first referral,
the operation being carried out the following day, and the patient
sent home very quickly before feelings of guilt have had time to
develop, or, (ii) to take time, to consult with colleagues and seek
further opinions and to re-interview the patient on a number of
occasions. The second of these approaches is generally preferred,
and in the case under discussion an interval of two and a half
weeks elapsed between first referral and operation – a fairly typical
time-lapse in National Health Service practice.

Not only from the point of view of what is decided, but also from
that of planning the general management of the situation and that

of the ultimate outcome in terms of health or morbidity, one of the most important considerations may be whether a case is conducted as a 'quickie' or as a more protracted affair. This reflects, in part, the professional identity and the stereotypes of behaviour of the individuals concerned. The gynaecologist will see in his out-patient practice mainly those who can be assessed quite quickly; indeed the Royal College of Obstetricians and Gynaecologists' Inquiry complains that the initial assessment of a case for termination may take 'as long as thirty minutes' and this may cause serious dislocation of his other work.[10] On the other hand, a social worker or a psychiatrist may tend by professional habit to see the pregnancy (whether aborted or not) as one, but only one, significant event in the continuing story of the patient's life. The behavioural stereotype of such a professional may be towards supporting her through a pregnancy and puerperium – a task lasting a year or more. How far might a difference in time perspective be influential in the decision-making process?

That the non-clinical attitudes of gynaecologists (and, of course, others) are important is illustrated by the 'inside story' of how it came about that the gynaecologist in Case I was presented with two conflicting recommendations, one from a social worker and the other from a psychiatrist. The social worker was new and when her report was taken to the gynaecologist in the out-patients department it created complete confusion because his name had been incorrectly spelled! The senior social worker was summoned to calm the electric atmosphere but the carefully argued social worker's report was brusquely rejected.

This also demonstrates the conflict of roles which may beset the gynaecologist. Not only is he a dispassionate assessor of the situation, but he may suddenly obtain an accession of power as an arbitrator between opposing interests and also he is the technician who will carry out the job. Beyond this again he has a responsibility for his own clinical team, and cannot be uninfluenced by the ethical scruples of his anaesthetist and the nursing staff in his theatres and wards. This point, incidentally, is a reminder that an abortion is in important respects a *social* event.

5. *Social workers, psychiatrists, etc.* Much of what has been written about the gynaecologist applies also to those who are taken into the situation in consultation. Like the gynaecologist, these people have their professional stereotypes. Supposing, then, there was a different balance of power. What different decisions, or diff-

erent reasons for decisions, might obtain if instead of visiting a hospital to see a doctor, the patient came initially to see the medical social worker who could then call in a gynaecologist for technical advice and help if she thought fit? Like the gynaecologist, they have sometimes conflicting roles, as assessors, as proxies for society at large or for the foetus, and they may be actors in the previous or subsequent management of the patient, whichever way the decision goes.

In a brief paper 'Account of the Environment'. published on the very day the Abortion Act came into effect, the principal medical social worker of a leading London maternity hospital[11] discusses the need to look behind the request for a termination to attempt to discover other needs which it may conceal, the necessity to keep in touch with the patient with sufficient consistency to be able to do something about them, the difficulty of listing the social and psychological factors which may be presented in support of such a request, and the technical problem of making a '. . . social evaluation while under considerable pressure in terms of time, stress, and emotional atmosphere, yet at the same time giving the patient the feeling that the investigation is disinterested and thorough'.

In Case I it is arguable that the patient was not helped adequately in the first place. She had three different social workers, one in each pregnancy. Perhaps she could have been seen at the outset to be a person with great problems in relation to men and she could have received more help with this both during and after the first pregnancy. It might possibly have been foreseen that she would land in the same trouble again, but the social worker had been 'clinically' orientated, i.e. in dealing only with the present pregnancy instead of looking beyond this into the patient's wider situation.

Against this is the fact that some families are unable to accept the form of further help or advice they are offered. In this case does the doctor or the social worker have any right to persist in the situation?

General comment on the participants in the decision. It is apparent that, appearances notwithstanding, the questions leading up to a decision about termination of pregnancy are never for an individual, but always for a number of people. The decision takes place within a social unit. Between those involved there may be a struggle for power, and this, unless acknowledged, could influence the decision which is finally made. It is clear too that there are different kinds of contribution to the decision-making process. We can distinguish at least two – those contributions which are ultimately determinative of the decision, and those which support or authorize action without necessarily determining it. It is worth noting that the Abortion Act does not require the two practitioners who sign the Notification Form to be determiners of the decisions. An abortion would not be illegal if they are simply authorizers – although many doctors would, of course, consider this an unacceptable surrender of power; and conventional medical ethics require that the technician performing any operation should also be one of the determiners of the decision.

The Circumstances of the Decision

It is clear that the circumstances in which the decision regarding termination is made will affect the decision. In Case II, for example, one view would be that the patient should have been admitted to allow the assessment and the decision to be made in the calmer atmosphere of in-patient care. The doctor sometimes has the duty of protecting the patient from family pressures. On the other hand it may be held that an adequate interview should suffice to uncover and to allow for the family pressures. It may, in any case, be proper to take the family pressures into account to some extent, and the manoeuvre of admitting the patient does have the effect of exposing her to the ethical and other arguments of the hospital staff.

Another illustration of the effects of situation upon decision-making is the not uncommon experience that the same social worker who successfully helps many clients to come to terms with pregnancies, which they had not expected and did not initially want, when working in one setting (perhaps a psychiatric clinic) may be quite unable to do this in another situation (such as a Pregnancy Advisory Service Clinic) where her efforts are simply seen as preventing the clients from using a facility to which they feel themselves entitled.

Power, Responsibility and a Relevant Ethic

The professional stereotype of the doctor would probably be to be 'clinical', and by this would be meant that he would try to be relatively free of values. The case would be decided by estimating the likely consequences of each indication and contra-indication pre-

sent in the situation and by balancing these one against the other.
There is, of course, the familiar difficulty in conducting controlled
investigations in this field – no one will ever know in an individual
case what would have happened if the action taken had been
other than it were. Nevertheless, information of a sort is available,
and the doctor's power within the social unit making the decision
seems to derive largely from this knowledge.

But the Abortion Act calls upon the doctor for the expression of
an 'opinion' – he is more than a repository of textbook knowledge.
He also plays the role of proxy for society at large, and society
has *values*. Now it has long been agreed among philosophers that
no number of facts can in the end yield the values by which a
decision is made. The grounds for the choice as to whether or not
to terminate a pregnancy include both facts and values, the dilemma
of the tough- and tender-minded decisions referred to earlier. The
problem is that of converting into a psychological–medical discussion, one that is to an important extent a social–ethical discussion.
One sometimes gets the impression that the medical machinery
for dealing with this situation is creaking somewhat.

That element in the power exercised by the doctor, which he
derives as a mediator of social values, he shares with others (including maybe the patient and her family) in the decision-making
unit. He does not, of course, have the same exclusive right to it
as the right based upon professional knowledge. But more importantly, no one in the situation has any *a priori* rights, but only in so
far as these are conferred upon him by society. We must therefore
consider the contribution of the culture at large to the abortion
decision.

In Case II, for example, an important consideration was the
woman's ability to provide adequate mothering for a large family.
Studies of large families show an increased incidence of failure to
cope among families where there are more than four children
under the age of five years. Personal inadequacy in the mother
becomes strikingly more significant in families larger than this.[12]
But here is also an example of the power of the professions to
influence culture. Suppose it became generally accepted in society
that women with more than four children were *ipso facto* unable
to cope, and this view were regularly authenticated by 'those who
know' (i.e. the doctors and social workers) aborting most pregnancies in excess of this number, is it not likely that women with
large families would thereby *become* less able to cope? Concepts

like 'difficulty in coping' or 'an unwanted pregnancy' are difficult to define with accuracy and their content is largely a matter of social consensus.

How then may a relevant system of values, a relevant ethic, be derived? In posing the question in this way it is assumed that ethical ideas are social products. They arise as part of a particular style of life. Where a woman presents herself for consideration for an abortion, the foetus has, as we have seen, become a symbol for her and her family of 'something gone wrong', of a threatened departure from their usual style of life. The choice before her – to keep the pregnancy or to end it – is a very radical choice in that it holds out the possibility of substantially changing her style of life. The situation is one of crisis. An ethical solution to her predicament is, it is suggested, one which enables all those concerned to develop their life style, whether this is a decision for termination or against. A successful decision changes perspectives, and responsible action on the part of the professionals involved is such action as permits this. There are thus no absolute ethical principles in matters of detail, but only an over-riding obligation to permit the actors in the situation to resolve their crisis in a way that leads to further growth and development rather than confirming them in their previous attitudes.

The question of saving (or not saving) the woman from the feelings of guilt that she seemed to have experienced, and which are of course not uncommon,[13] can now be seen in a different light. Probably every genuine moral choice is accompanied by some doubt and uncertainty – if not, it is scarcely likely to have been a moral choice. We need to distinguish between guilt and doubt. In the former the patient says 'I have done wrong' but in the latter she says 'I do not know whether I have done right or wrong'. It is not easy to know how clearly this distinction was made in those accounts that have been published of the patients' reactions following termination. Guilt or mourning or doubt are in themselves morally neither good nor bad and a procedure cannot be condemned merely because it does, or does not, produce a particular emotional response.

This paper is written from a 'moderate' point of view, that is that some requests for termination of pregnancy based on psychological and social grounds should properly be granted and some should properly be rejected. However, this viewpoint leads to complex social and ethical considerations. These may be better managed, but not of course avoided, by a clearer understanding of the processes involved in reaching the decision.

Postscript

This paper, the outcome of a discussion in a local Field Group of the Institute of Religion and Medicine, is reprinted here not only for its intrinsic interest, but also as an example of the kind of trans-disciplinary consultation which the Institute seeks to foster. The approach to a topic such as abortion by an I. R. M. Group should differ from that of a professional body of, say, gynaecologists or lawyers in that its primary aim should be to illuminate the reciprocal relationship between, on the one hand, professional knowledge and technique and, on the other, a philosophical or theological interpretation of the nature of man. Insofar as the present paper attempts to do this, its content is relatively independent of the vagaries of public opinion. Nevertheless, although the form of the decision-making process remains unchanged, the weight given to the various factors taken into account within it will be influenced by the information, attitudes and values current in society at the time of the decision.

The original discussion took place in February 1970 at which time uncertainty about the operation of the Abortion Act was at its height, and there was comparatively little published material around which a professional consensus might develop. Such a situation naturally stimulated the production of a considerable literature. Rather than attempt any revision of the paper as originally published, the editor has permitted this postscript, written in April 1972, to call attention to some sources of information and attitudes which have become available in the interval. It is hoped that this may be of value to any readers who are reconsidering this matter.

Comprehensive statistical information about notified abortions (for 1970 – the most recent year for which figures have been published) is available in pamphlet form as part of the Registrar General's review of the year.[14] Included in this is an analysis of the medical and environmental grounds upon which abortions were carried out. Also in pamphlet form is a brief factual review of the working of the Act published by the Advisory Group on Sex, Marriage and the Family of the British Council of Churches.[15] A very much more substantial account of this material, with several

hundred references to the literature, is provided in Horden's book
Legal Abortion: The English Experience.[16] An example of one
man's thinking on the relationship between practice and faith is
Gardner's *Abortion: The Personal Dilemma* – subtitled *A Christian
gynaecologist examines the medical, social and spiritual issues.*[17]
Finally, a collection of essays written from an American background *The Morality of Abortion; Legal and Historical Perspectives*[18] is equally pertinent to the British scene.

Acknowledgements

The author is deeply indebted to the members of the Study Group
in which this paper originated. They will, however, see that the
material has been adapted for publication, and he must therefore
accept sole responsibility for its final form.

NOTES

1. P. Diggory, J. Peel, and M. Potts, 'Preliminary Assessment of the 1967
Abortion Act in Practice', *Lancet*, 1970, Part I, pp.287–91.

2. *Abortion Act 1967*.

3. Royal College of Obstetricians and Gynaecologists, 'The Abortion Act
1967. Findings of an Inquiry into the First Year's Working of the Act',
British Medical Journal, 1970, Part 2, pp.529–35.

4. *Hansard* (1971) 812, 313 (23 February).

5. *Abortion Act, 1967*.

6. M. P. Oates, 'A Medical Social Worker's View of the Termination of
Pregnancy Act 1967', *Midland Medical Review*, Vol. 6, 1970, pp.84–89.

7. D. M. Johnson, *The Psychology of Thought and Judgement*, Harper,
1955 see Chaps. 9 and 10.

8. Johnson, *op. cit.*, p.296.

9. A. F. Coward, 'A comparison of Two Methods of Grading English
Compositions', *Journal of Educational Research*, Vol. 46, 1952, pp.81–93.

10. Royal College of Obstetricians and Gynaecologists, *Op. cit.*, p.533.

11. N. M. Cogan, 'Account of the Environment. A Medical Social Worker
looks at the new Abortion Law', *British Medical Journal*, 1968, Part I,
pp.235-6.

12. P. C. Shapiro, Personal Communication.

13. M. Clarke, I. Forstner, D. A. Pond, and R. F. Tredgold, 'Sequels of
Unwanted Pregnancy', *Lancet*, 1968, Part 2, pp.501–3.

14. Office of Population Censuses and Surveys, *The Registrar General's
Statistical Review of England and Wales for the Year 1970. Supplement
on Abortion*, London: H.M.S.O. 1972.

15. British Council of Churches, *The Abortion Act 1967–69; A Factual
Review*, Witney Press, 1970.

16. A. Horden, *Legal Abortion; The English Experience*, Pergamon, 1971.

17. R. F. R. Gardner, *Abortion; The Personal Dilemma*, Paternoster Press, 1972.

18. J. T. Noonan, *The Morality of Abortion; Legal and Historical Perspectives*, Harvard University Press, 1970.

10 Can the Community Care?

Sydney Brandon

Dr Brandon is Reader in Psychiatry in the University of Manchester and Consultant Psychiatrist to Manchester Royal Infirmary and Withington Hospital. He has written on epidemiology, community care, drug abuse, social deviance and institutionalism.

This article is based upon an address given to the Manchester branch of the Institute at Manchester in April 1971.

We are in medicine, a long established, generally respected and uniquely personal profession, whose concern is primarily with the individual. Our practitioners are often unrepentant individualists and we have achieved as a profession a unique power and independence in determining our own patterns of practice, in maintaining standards and in developing our own ethical code over several generations. Despite doubts about the future of general practice and criticisms regarding the National Health Service the model usually considered in discussing the delivery of medical care is that of the general practitioner standing in personal relationship to his patient.

The unique character of our National Health Service lies in the fact that our general practitioner service accepts responsibility for every member of the community. In theory at least, every individual in this country is the responsibility of a named general medical practitioner. The importance of this fact, especially in considering the care of the chronic sick and the more deprived members of our community, cannot be over emphasized and it is this more than anything else which distinguishes our service from that provided by other countries. A psychiatrist working in the United States is faced, when he considers discharging from a state hospital a chronic schizophrenic patient, with the real prospect of his patient being unable to find a doctor who will look after such a troublesome, uneconomical, unrewarding customer. He has no assurance that his patient will receive regular medication let alone regular supervision. Despite obvious strengths the whole future of general practice as we know it has been open to question.

A good deal of the criticisms of the general practitioner service have arisen as a consequence of our failure to recognize changing moods in both our patients and our doctors. Much of our thinking about the general practitioner services is based upon a pattern of practice which probably no longer exists. We are talking in terms of the country practitioner, a man living in a small community with intimate knowledge of patients whom he has delivered and nurtured and cared for since they were young. He is seen as a man widely respected and integrated into all aspects of community life, usually as a more educated member of society, better informed over a wide range of affairs than most of the individuals for whom he is providing care, yet a man of sufficient leisure and concern to spend a great deal of time with his patients and to discuss with them a wide range of problems going far beyond concern for the simple delivery of medical care. He is confidante, mentor and guide to his patients.

Clearly, this is an ideal state and in the writings of general practitioners such as Pickles of Wensleydale[1] we can see the immense satisfactions provided by this kind of practice, but few general practitioners now have had such experience. Increasing urbanization, increasing mobility, smaller families, the attenuation of the kinship system, and the fact that some ten per cent of a general practitioner's list changes each year mean that in many cases the general practitioner is unable to identify with a specific area. His practice ranges over a number of urban rather than rural districts with a good deal of overlap between practices and members of one family scattered on several doctors' lists. Very often, the general practitioner presented with a patient in his consulting room is dealing with a stranger and yet our discussion of the nature of general practice often ignores this fact.

The fact, too, that the general practitioner himself has needs is often forgotten. He no longer provides a twenty-four hour service to his patient. He often practises as a member of a group and in addition to the rota system there is often a system of night calls dealt with by an impersonal call service, while hospital referral is increasingly common and a wide range of other professionals are often involved in the provision of care.

Over many years the main tool in the therapeutic armoury of the doctor has been his own personality, yet this received scant attention in either selection or training. In the past the charismatic authority of the doctor has been the foundation of the patient–doctor relationship but in recent decades this has suffered many strains. Higher levels of sophistication, education and expectation among our patients have resulted in the considerable narrowing of the gap of knowledge between practitioner and patient not only in general, but in the body of knowledge of medicine itself. Many of us have had the latest advance in a particular area of medicine presented to us by one of our patients, whose source was the Sunday colour supplement or *Reader's Digest*. This wide dissemination of health information results in our patients being well informed in many aspects of care and consequently questioning, examining and criticizing our advice and care in a way which was unknown to the last generation.

Our patients have also become increasingly sophisticated in their expectations of medical care and in the demands which they make upon us. The pattern of practice to which we so nostalgically refer, in which the doctor cared for a comparatively small number of patients to whom he was able to devote a great deal of attention, was only possible in rural districts where the number of people was comparatively small but where there was sufficient wealth to pay private fees which subsidized the rest of the practice. In the large urban areas, many patients were entirely without medical care or were dependent upon dispensaries and other forms of voluntary medical care, or upon various workers' schemes which were eventually incorporated into the national insurance plan which represented a considerable advance in the delivery of care. Even in 1947 a large segment of the population of this country was completely cut off from medical care except in extremis. In a survey of a group of children in Newcastle in 1947[2] one of the most striking observations was the reluctance of the parents of young children to call in a doctor because of the expense and difficulties which surrounded such a consultation. This formed a very striking contrast to the pattern of care which infants received a decade later after the introduction of the National Health Service.[3]

The National Health Service has made available to everyone the standards of medical care which were previously only accessible to the middle and upper classes. This has made enormous demands upon resources and involved substantial re-adjustments in the organization of care which have evolved from necessity rather than planning. Implications of some of these developments have still not been properly examined.

Until recently there has been little emphasis in our training of doctors upon the development of the patient–doctor relationship or on the use of the self. In the past, a stethoscope was an accepted symbol of wisdom and authority which invested the doctor with an aura which was his to use. Today it is not uncommon to have patients reject the doctor's diagnosis and question his treatment or to have relatives advise the sick to stay away from 'pill pushers'. More than ever before the practitioner stands dependent upon his own personal resources. Our graduates are still comparatively ill-equipped in terms of making psycho-social assessments and evaluations, and yet our patients and society are defining an increasingly widening range of dis-ease, unhappiness and maladjustment as medical problems. Without the intimate knowledge of the patient and his social milieu which our model country general practitioner would have had, the contemporary urban practitioner is presented with a bewildering range of moral, psychological, social and sexual problems.

Apart from his limited training and perhaps limited inclination, the time to deal with these problems is simply not available. To provide this universally available service with ever increasing level of demands, the medical resources in this country are now, and in the foreseeable future will continue to be, inadequate. We have in medicine in general, and in psychiatry in particular, over-sold our skills and so widened our range of interest and concern as to lead sometimes to unrealistic expectations among our patients. Our failure to deal with many of the psychological, social and sexual problems of patients is no doubt one of the factors which have led to the somewhat concealed, but nevertheless real, criticisms of patterns of medical practice incorporated for instance in the Seebohm Report[4] and which have resulted in various other developments tending to isolate medical practice.

Let us now consider the demands upon resources resulting from psychiatric illness. One problem to be faced is the basic one of defining psychiatric illness. Some practitioners prefer the view of Psychiatry Limited and believe that psychiatrists should limit their concern to those with diseases or disorders of mind which can be defined in medical terms as illness. The Psychiatry Unlimited view holds, in its extreme claims, that the psychiatrist has a body of knowledge and skills which enable him to contribute to every aspect of life. This view would hold that the Psychiatric Society for the Prevention of War is as appropriate as the Psychosomatic Society.

In the end it is society or the community itself which sets the limits and at present the profession is being asked to define in psychiatric terms a wide range of behaviours. Even taking a more limited view, however, and confining ourselves to conspicuous psychiatric morbidity the burden is a considerable one.

In a well organized general practice with an appointments system the time allowed for face to face contact between doctor and patient is of the order of seven minutes. It is difficult for a psychiatrist to see how it is possible to make an adequate psychiatric assessment in less than thirty-five minutes or five patient spaces. It has been estimated that one person in seven on a practitioners list will consult him each year with a significant psychiatric illness. Thus a practitioner with a list of two and a half thousand would expect to see a new psychiatric case each day. If he found some magic formula by which he could in the course of six fifteen-minute sessions cure each of these patients he would spend more than half of his working day in dealing with psychiatric problems, which make up only a modest part of the spectrum of medical care.

Psychiatry has undergone an explosive expansion in terms of numbers and resources since the inception of the National Health Service yet still requires further investment. Recognition of this need led to serious consideration that psychiatric services should be excluded from the National Health Service at its inception as it is from many private insurance schemes in countries such as the United States.

At present the psychiatric services deal with only ten per cent of cases identified by the general practitioner as psychiatrically ill, yet are fully extended and painfully aware of deficiencies arising from lack of professional time. At present we have one psychiatrist to 50,000 of our population which could be expected, according to reliable general practice based research,[5] to generate an annual prevalence of 295 cases of major psychosis, 115 of mental subnormality, 70 of dementia, 4,225 of neurosis and 275 of major personality disorder. There is little prospect of the development of 'luxury services' such as psychotherapy in the face of these work loads.

Formal psychiatric illness constitutes only one area of demand for we are now seeing the development of patterns of ill health or maladjustment in the community, which are increasingly defined as psychiatric but which cannot be satisfactorily handled within the traditional psychiatric system. The current major epidemic facing Western society is attempted suicide – perhaps more accurately described as self-poisoning or para suicide.[6] There has been a steep escalation of this pattern of behaviour over the past twenty years and in our major cities about one in every thousand of the population will attempt to injure themselves each year. Between ten to fifteen per cent of acute admissions to medical wards arise from self-poisoning and each presents a complex psycho-social problem which, according to instructions from the Ministry of Health, should be assessed by a psychiatrist before the patient leaves hospital.

Alcoholism probably occurs in one per cent of the population and generates in its wake a complex of organic and social problems. The consequences of drug abuse, the increasing emergence of problems of sexuality, and awareness of the need for family, child and adolescent psychiatric services demand not only more time and resources but fundamental reappraisal of the nature of the service to be provided.

Following the loss of a loved, or indeed of an unloved, close relative or associate the work of grief goes on to recognize and fill the void created. It has long been recognized that grief may merge into illness and there has been some suggestion that pathological or distorted grieving is more common than in the past. Geoffrey Gorer,[7] among others, has suggested that the reduction of the ritual of mourning and the lesser acquaintance with death, which results from smaller families and improved life expectation, and the attenuation of family and neighbourhood network results in increasing denial of grief and consequently an increase in pathological patterns with an increase in the development of significant illness.[7] We simply do not have comparative data with which to support or reject this hypothesis but there is adequate documentation of the fact that bereavement is followed by a significant increase in morbidity and even mortality. There is a sharp increase in medical consultation rates for a wide variety of disorders not only psychiatric illness but physical conditions not usually regarded as having psychological antecedents.[8] That divorce and marital breakdown have similar patterns of increased morbidity[9] is scarcely surprising but it is less well recognized that disasters such as the Bristol floods have the same sequelae.[10]

Awareness of the social and psychological disturbances associated with child bearing has been increasing over the years. Puerperal psychosis is more readily recognized and treated in many cases without separation of mother and infant. The problems of adjustment to pregnancy, delivery and motherhood, psychoprophylaxis in labour and the diverse problems arising from unwanted pregnancy are less readily identified but it is evident that there is a need for clearer identification of the problems involved and considerable need for services not currently provided. Again it appears that these needs have become more apparent as a consequence of changes in the patterns of society particularly in the way in which the young are exposed to life experiences and supported by family networks during their own early experiences.

With the established and increasing psychiatric case load we can look hopefully at the prospects of the prevention of mental disorder. Unfortunately there is little clear evidence that primary prevention – the prevention of the occurrence of disease – is yet feasible in the field of psychiatry. Secondary prevention – the prevention of disability by decreasing the severity or shortening the duration of illness – is dependent on the effectiveness of our treatment services. The most clearly demonstrated area of effect is in tertiary prevention, that is, the prevention of disability arising from the experience of illness but not intrinsic to it. In schizophrenia the reduction of residual disability through active treatment and rehabilitation in the community is truly dramatic and in this common and chronic disorder represents a major achievement.

Turning to the less well defined dis-eases the provision of treatment or support undoubtedly reduces human distress and suffering but we can not yet be certain that it results in any reduction in the prevalence of disease. In these borderlands of pathology the psychiatrist and his discipline have important contributions to offer but society as a whole may be a more effective therapist.

For example, the 1775 liquor tax put an end to Gin Lane and Hogarthian drunkenness while I suspect that the 1914 Licensing Acts had more effect upon the prevalence of alcoholism than all our alcoholism treatment units. At the stroke of an administrator's pen an explosive and destructive epidemic of intravenous methidrine abuse was terminated because the drug was no longer available.

Direct community action of a different kind has influenced attempted suicide which has absorbed an enormous investment of medical resources without any noticeable effect on the continued escalation of the epidemic. Many of the so called suicide attempts are labelled as trivial or manipulative because the medical risk to life seems low but this is no guide to the seriousness of the attempt. A lovers' tiff may lead to death or prolonged resuscitation in a respiratory unit whereas a desperate individual bent on self destruction may find that the chosen method fails completely. Any individual who engages in deliberate self-poisoning enters a high risk group with a considerably increased risk of repetition of the behaviour and more than one in ten will die within the next five to ten years.

Anyone who plays this hazardous game is at the time distressed and in need. Usually it is a call for help, sometimes an angry impulse, but it was the distress which led Chad Varah to establish the Telephone Samaritan service. The attitude of doctors in general and psychiatrists in particular to this 'do-gooder' organization varied from open hostility to amused scepticism. The plan was simple – that is the Samaritan, an untrained psychiatrically unsophisticated volunteer, should befriend the client and offer an opportunity to the client, not to talk to, but to be listened to, as well as encouragement, support, persuasion that things were perhaps not hopeless after all but no practical help was to be offered.

Christopher Bagley[11] has confounded predictions by demonstrating in a scientifically impeccable study that in those areas in which Samaritan services have been introduced there has been a slowing or reversal of the national trend in suicide and attempted suicide. We are now the only nation in Western Europe with a declining suicide rate and though the detoxication of domestic coal gas is an important factor a major share of the credit must go to the Samaritans.

If, as I am suggesting, medicine is unable to cope with all the problems with which society is presenting us, can we not turn to society itself for increasing help? Attempted suicide, alcoholism, drug abuse, the problems of childhood and adolescence, the despair of bereavement, the fears, fantasies and hopes of pregnancy and childbirth and the loneliness and isolation experienced by many patients before they present with major psychiatric breakdowns are often associated with impaired interpersonal relationships, inadequate family and neighbourhood supports and many developing problems show a dramatic improvement in response to simple befriending and neighbourly behaviour.

In our urban society with small family groups, stretched family networks and environmental designs which discourage social interaction, we need to concentrate upon the development of helping networks within the community which can offer companionship, support, guidance and constraints to fellow-community members who without such help are in danger of failing to cope with their life situation in a way which will eventually bring them into the orbit of medicine. Only if the community can care can medicine cope.

Medicine must learn to work in partnership with a variety of community agencies both statutory and voluntary, formal and informal. We must learn to appreciate and use the skills of other professionals but more and more we must relearn the art of consultation and enable others to carry out tasks which may be identified by doctors but do not require the skill of the physician. Techniques such as crisis intervention can be widely disseminated, longer term support offering substitute mothering or more directive fathering can be provided by anyone who can combine informed common sense and real concern.

The community is involved in medicine in many other ways. It is clear that medicine cannot provide a truly comprehensive service in which every development is available to all in need and priorities must be set on purely economic grounds. We cannot go on developing intensive care units, new techniques of transplantation and new drugs with the resources currently available. As war is too important to be left to the generals so medicine is too important to all of us to be left entirely to the doctors and the community must play its part in allocating priorities within medicine.

The actual pattern of practice is, as we have discussed, influenced by community attitudes such as the fashions in illness behaviour like attempted suicide. Pressure groups in society can modify medical practice and indeed medical ethics. The Mental Health Act 1959, was considerably in advance of both professional and public attitudes but radically changed the patterns of practice. The Abortion Act, 1967, changed not only practice but medical ethics for here attitudes and opinions in the community have imposed upon a somewhat reluctant profession new criteria of judgment in what was previously an ethical matter.

This raises some fundamental problems for medicine because in the past physicians have had virtually exclusive rights in determining their corporate ethics. Medicine has maintained an ethical code publicly enforced and maintained but largely determined by a small group of doyens of the profession.

In abortion we have an example of a community imposed alteration of practice occurring with due process of law. While medicine must be subject to the law it seems reasonable that individual practitioners should have the right to exercise a conscience clause and refuse to participate in acts which conflict with their beliefs. Such opting out should of course be clearly stated from the beginning and cannot be partial or conditional. The Abortion Act in fact did little more than codify a pattern of practice that had been gradually evolving but it does raise fundamental issues.

What should happen if parliament were to impose a pattern of practice entirely repugnant to the majority of the profession? It has been suggested in discussion of the Abortion Act that we can ignore the law or manipulate it according to our own inclinations. I suggest that this is a mistaken view and that we must accept the law of the land, opting out on grounds of conscience if appropriate, and seeking, ourselves as a pressure group, the support of the community in securing a change in the law.

Among other problems of medical ethics which have come to the attention of the community recently is the thorny one of confidentiality. This becomes increasingly important if, as I have suggested, medicine becomes more concerned with the development of para-medical and voluntary services within the community. The rights of the individual to confidentiality, the limits of confidentiality when the welfare of others is involved and the extent to which sharing can occur with others concerned in the care of the patient need to be clarified. We certainly need to review the circumstances in which it is possible for a general practitioner deliberately to engage in a breach of confidence with a young person just under the age of eighteen when the Latey committee, the law and the British Medical Association all clearly state that on attaining the age of sixteen years a person is entitled to complete confidentiality and is entirely competent in seeking treatment in his own right.

Another ethical problem which has recently troubled me is that apparent neglect of the basic concept that medicine is practised regardless of caste, creed or political affiliation. We have recently heard of doctors declining to provide medical services to strikers, boys with long hair and to communists. Our medical ethical system because of its long history is often taken as a model by other professions but this has only served to emphasize that, like our own concepts of general practice, our ethical practice is no longer entirely appropriate to the age in which we live.

In this somewhat discursive review I have tried to express some of my thoughts about the relationship between medicine and the community. I believe that we are moving from the practice of personal, individual medicine to the practice of community medicine in which respect for the individual is maintained, and I suggest that good community medicine can only evolve if the community is involved.

NOTES

1. William Norman Pickles, *Epidemiology in Country Practice*, Bristol, John Wright Ltd, 1939.

2. J. C. Spence, W. S. Walton, F. J. W. Miller and S. D. M. Court. *A Thousand Families in Newcastle upon Tyne*, Oxford University Press, 1954.

3. F. J. W. Miller, S. D. M. Court, S. Walton and E. J. Knox, *Growing up in Newcastle*, Oxford University Press, 1960.

4. *Report of the Committee on Local Authority and Allied Personal Social Services*, H.M.S.O., 1968.

5. M. Shepherd, M. Cooper, A. C. Brown and G. W. Kalton, *Psychiatric illness in general practice*, Oxford University Press, 1966.

6. N. Kessel, 'Self-poisoning', *British Medical Journal*, 1965, part 2, pp.1235–1236.

7. G. Gorer, *Death, Grief and Mourning*, Cresset Press, 1965.

8. C. M. Parkes. 'Effects of bereavement on physical and mental health', *British Medical Journal*, 1964, part 2, p.274.

9. R. Chester, 'Health and Marriage Breakdown', *British Journal of Preventive and Social Medicine*, vol. 25, 1971, p.231.

10. G. Bennet, 'Bristol Floods 1968. Controlled Survey of Effects on Health of local Community Disaster', *British Medical Journal*, 1970, part 3, p.454.

11. C. Bagley, 'The Evaluation of a Suicide Prevention Scheme by an Ecological Method', *Social Science and Medicine*, vol. 2, 1968, p.1.

11 A Psychiatrist's Impression of the Client/Samaritan Inter-Action

T. E. Lear

Dr T. E. Lear is Psychiatric Tutor in the Northampton/Kettering area and he leads a Psychotherapy Seminar for psychiatrists. He is Consultant in the Northampton psychiatric service and to a social service family centre.

This chapter is based on a paper given to the Northampton Branch of the Samaritans in May 1971.

What can be generalized about the client-Samaritan relationship? First it is a dialogue between two people and what we call a one-to-one relationship. It is particularly private because the Samaritan has no doorman and so no intermediate person – the client makes direct contact with the Samaritan by calling on the telephone or by calling in. Availability is immediate and the already upset person does not have more than one struggle if this is his experience with starting a relationship. This person does not have the disadvantage of being a patient which may place him in a rather regressed position. He does not necessarily expect the Samaritan to do something to him or for him but rather the opportunity is for him to discuss something for himself. Furthermore he does not have the disadvantage of becoming a psychiatric patient and taking on a burden of stigma in addition to his other worries, nor the fear that he may be going mad or that he may be shut away in a mental hospital with all his apprehension about that place. A professional person might learn a lot by working as a Samaritan, to compare the relationship work in a different non-professional setting. If he or she phones there are only auditory cues and no visual information. We had a telephone seminar once which was a weekly discussion using a special apparatus so that doctors in London and Northampton could discuss and I found this a strain at times.

Not very long ago I visited a drug addiction unit in a London teaching hospital. After talking with people I knew in the psychiatric department I crossed the road to look for a former colleague in this drug addiction unit. I had not visited this part of the hospital previously and my curiosity was aroused and in I walked. Almost immediately a nursing sister came up. There was something in her manner which showed me an opportunity. She asked me if this was my first visit and I said it was and that I would like to see around. She did not ask my name or business but proceeded to show me the place and to introduce some of the people there. I do not know if she felt I was seeking help or guessed I was a professional person and wanted to show me her technique but I was not going to spoil the privilege of seeing how she was working. In this experience I felt welcome, supported and challenged – it was an experience of being held. The nursing sister seemed close to me but not in an embarrassing way. I felt I could talk with her and it was not for long that I held out on her and quite soon I said why I had come and it so happened that my friend was not there.

Nurses, particularly psychiatric nurses, are skilled with this friendly, wise, close holding with people who come into the psychiatric ward and I imagine that this holding operation is an important part of the Samaritans' work at the beginning as well. Keeping the person with you while you have time to build up trust. Sometimes in the general hospital when talking with someone who has attempted suicide and might do so again I have a fantasy of that person's fantasy of being held by me or the family doctor or people in the family or a social worker until the next contact with one or some of these people. In other words, I try to get an impression of how much care this person needs and how much is available and whether I should make an intervention or not to increase this. Here are some of these points in starting a relationship.

1. By being available immediately.
2. Friendly and welcoming tone in the voice.
3. Avoid asking a lot of questions which might be too challenging.
4. Listening and making clear in what you say that you are listening and going along with this person's story.
5. Trying to get close without being over familiar and here you have the advantage that you have no professional aura

or uniform to cause a distance between you and your client.*

6. Having a role like an older brother or sister who is wise but not judgmental and moreover one who is firm and hopeful.

During an interview the interviewer has three questions:

A. What is this person saying and how does he or she seem to feel?
B. How does this person make me feel?
C. What about this person's situation?

At the same time the interviewer assumes that it is both true that this person wishes to be helped or rescued (after all he phones or makes contact) and that he wishes to kill himself—the chances of this would be termed the lethality. Thus in considering these three aspects of the interview the interviewer keeps these possibilities in mind and watches the balance as well.

---

* Recently I was asked to talk with a young, married woman in the medical ward after her third suicide attempt. We were shown to the linen cupboard on the ward because there were no other interview facilities. This illustrates by the way the social stigma of suicide for although attempted suicides amount to about ten to fifteen per cent of medical ward admissions there are no proper facilities for this work. Psychiatrists tend to be regarded as disposal agents rather than carrying out important work in the ward. Some doctors and nurses do not seem to see a job beyond resuscitation and become irritated when they do not see a cause for illness and are rather scornful sometimes about what seems a self-inflicted situation. After years of plugging away by psychiatrists through various channels at long last I am pleased to say that there is some hope of improvement in the general hospital facilities in this area.

Returning to our interview in the linen cupboard, imagine the setting with this woman sitting in a wheelchair with nightdress and dressing gown, with me sitting opposite in my suit in the narrow space of the cupboard. We were frequently interrupted by a succession of curious nurses who fussed to find some article on the shelf and then withdrew. Notice, however, the psychological closeness of this setting and how having been used to nurses in uniform and doctors in white coats on the ward, she was confronted by me in my old suit and she proceeded to pour out her troubles to me. Part of the work on that occasion was talking to her husband who seemed to reject her at first but wanted her home after further consideration. Later that week in the out patient clinic it was quite different. She was dressed in her usual clothes and her little boy was with her in the waiting room. When she came into my room she was silent and I felt there was considerable distance between us and it was not until I drew attention to the very different circumstances in which we were meeting from the last occasion that she smiled and began to thaw out but it was not until the next interview that she could begin to talk frankly with me again.

I shall first consider (A) in a general way: What is this person saying and how does he or she seem to feel?

There is a constellation of possible symptoms the four D's of Schneidman[1] (Dr Edwin Schneidman is chief of Centre for Studies of Suicide Prevention, National Institute of Mental Health, USA): depression, disoriented, defiant and dependent-dissatisfied.

1. *Depression* is the portrayal of bitter, sad or hopeless feelings in expression, tone of voice, posture and slowing of movements and speech which may be accompanied by body experiences like reduced appetites for food, sleep and sex and defaecation as well as reduced energy and interest. Paradoxically, lethality is inversely related to the intensity of these symptoms as if the risk of suicide increases as the internal energy to commit suicide becomes available. It follows that symptom change is not a good indicator for the helper to gauge his efforts and he must look for different factors before it is safe to slacken his care.

2. *Disoriented* means hearing voices or having false and even unlikely beliefs and so the person responds to his own internal cues of which the interviewer is more or less unaware. Suicidal notions from such a muddled person are to be regarded usually as a serious risk and the need for nursing care is probable. The psychiatrist is the agent to arrange this often through family doctor or mental health social worker.

3. *Defiant.* This is the sort of person who needs to control the interview and indeed his environment as if reflecting an inability to handle his inner stresses. Put differently a person may insist on his rights and privileges as if there is underlying doubt about them all the time. To jolly such a person makes matters worse but to be a willing target of aggressive and demanding behaviour may deflect his energy from suicide to be expended in this way.

4. *Dependent-dissatisfied.* This is a person who while realizing that he is ill feels he should not need help. There is a great need for care and attention. The interviewer gets challenged frequently with 'You don't believe me do you?' or 'I don't feel this is helping' or 'I just don't feel any better – I think I'm getting worse' or 'You can't help me, can you?' etc. This requires great patience and with the expression and sharing of his own inner feelings of desperation it is to be hoped that suicide may be prevented.

The second consideration is how does this person make me feel? There are times when I am made to feel helpless in an interview. Then I ask myself is this really beyond my help and should I request and enlist help from other professionals, notably nursing colleagues in the psychiatric ward or perhaps I do not accept that I am in fact helpless and see a possibility of helping this person. Often as a consultant I keep a middle distance with a person because I know that we shall not continue our relationship beyond a diagnostic interview. If this is a strain I take it as a good sign that this person can get into a closeness quickly. This feeling of hope with someone, particularly if you can continue with them, is something important and positive. It is your response to his need and his acceptance of your help. There are other people who I cannot stand but I ask nevertheless is he or she suicidal – if so then I transfer the care to one of those who can relate helpfully to this person.

One night recently the phone went at 5 a.m. and a Casualty Officer informed me that a young man in the General Hospital had cut his wrists and was wanting to leave for a further suicidal attempt. The social worker was not available just then and I went down to the Casualty Department. This time in the 24 hour clock is not my time of peak performance and I was approaching a young man who had caused me some discomfort. At the same time I was aware of his unhappy circumstances which amounted to a considerable suicide risk. Among various upsets in his life experience, there were disturbed relations at home and he really had nowhere to stay so that my job, as it turned out, was to prepare him for admission to a psychiatric ward where there would be nurses who could help.

It may be in discussion with another professional person that I come to terms with my feelings and then I am freed to help and this is the value of consultation or supervision. I try to be aware of my prejudices to some extent in order to deal with *recoil*.

Recoil is the immediate sense of dismay in the interviewer by a trigger impression from the person making contact. My heart sank when I heard him say,

> I'm on hard drugs
> or   I want to terminate my pregnancy
> or   I'm in trouble for indecent exposure
> or   I'm a member of A.A.
> or   It all started when my aged mother came to live with us
> or   I've just retired
> or   I've got a mentally handicapped child.

I could add to the list and so could others, and each person would have a different list. A second take is obviously important after the recoil so that the usual consideration with this person is possible.

Another recoil experience in the interviewer can occur when it is a prominent citizen or professional colleague and it is on the second take that this sort of person needs to be dealt with like any other client.

Sometimes a person may criticize a professional worker and even if the interviewer has a strong inclination to join with the criticism it should not deter him from seeking the appropriate assistance from the professional person. An unclear suspicion is probably a true suicide risk in these circumstances and appropriate steps should be taken to notify others, seeking consultation, alerting family or friends or getting someone to hospital. It is better to err on the liberal side even at the risk of becoming a nuisance to the professionals.

Before leaving the consideration of feelings in the interviewer, time and time again the desperate and suffering person will evoke suffering in the listener. There is in this interaction an implicit dialogue within the interviewer which goes something like this: 'Your suffering makes me uncomfortable. I shall show you that I can stand this discomfort so let's bear this suffering together.' The Reverend L. Turner tells me that this is pure theology. In any case, I imagine this to be the core of Samaritan work.

Now we come to our last question: What about this person's situation? This is what I call taking a cool look at the person's life circumstances. One day I was sitting opposite a man in a different general hospital ward but a similar linen cupboard. He was hopeful and said that his mood of despair had passed and that he reckoned he was fortunate because he had a good job for some years and although separated from his wife he was comfortable with his parents and one child after all was content with his wife and the other happy with his sister. He did not make me feel uneasy but I put the information which he gave me into the context of his own situation and it went something like this. Here is a man who had a marriage, children, his home, a job and independence to some extent from his early family. He still has his job but he lost his home, his wife, his children and to some extent his independent status in living with parents again. His job was not that rewarding and his relations with parents dubious. His losses were enormous and his assets meagre. I decided he was a serious suicide risk and offered admission to the psychiatric ward. It is often in reviewing the life situation that areas for discussion or case work can be identified.

Many professionals like family doctors who have an open ended opportunity with people and work at a fast pace leave it to the patient to select the life experience they wish to discuss in the brief time available. It is a call on interviewer's skills if work is to be segmental and the interviewer is to influence strongly the context of discussion and in these circumstances the interviewer is still using the cues given him by the person about the priority experiences for discussion. People experiencing a personal crisis need plenty of nursing care and I have heard the Reverend Gordon Ford say more than once that he regards the Samaritan Service as a lynch-pin of professional services. What I would say is that the Samaritan is making an intervention in a personal crisis and there is some evidence that a person in a crisis is more readily influenced and may emerge from the crisis towards health better equipped to deal with similar situations occurring again or the person may be unchanged when the crisis which may last up to six weeks has passed or lastly the person may be damaged in the crisis experience and remain more or less handicapped. Thus the Samaritan intervention may tip the balance towards health or illness at this crucial time.

NOTE

1. E. S. Schneidman, *The American Journal of Nursing*, vol. 5, 1965, pp.10–15.

I would suggest for further reading G. Caplan's *An Approach to Community Mental Health* (Tavistock Publications, 1961) and *Bulletin of Suicidology*, December 1968, pp.19–25.

12 Medico-Social Aspects of Industrial Welfare

(1) *H. A. F. Mackay*
(2) *J. S. Barlow*

This chapter is composed of two papers given at the 1970 Conference of the Institute of Religion and Medicine at Newcastle.

The first part is by Dr H. A. F. Mackay, a general practitioner in a group practice in County Durham, with a part-time appointment in industrial medicine.

The second part is by J. S. Barlow, who is Regional Training Officer in the Northern Region of the Department of Health and Social Security. He is an active Presbyterian layman.

1

My qualifications for writing this chapter are simply that I am a general practitioner with interest in and some experience of industrial health. The advantage of this dual experience is that as a general practitioner I deal with people in their home environment and as an industrial medical officer I deal with them in their industrial environment.

Some may have been slightly puzzled as to the precise meaning of the title of this chapter which indeed is capable of various interpretations. However, for the purpose of my contribution I have proposed to discuss the health aspects of the industrial environment and its effect upon workers. At this stage I would like to make the point that if this symposium is to have any significance we must accept the proposition that work is not merely an economic necessity which is sometimes unpleasant and at best tolerable but is part of the whole activity of man, which is both beneficial and desirable. If this is accepted then we should try and eliminate any factors which may adversely affect the individual as a personality, and this has particular relevance in the medical field.

There are three particular aspects which I would like to discuss briefly here.

A. *Medical fitness for work*

At first sight this would appear to be a relatively simple problem merely involving a strict medical assessment of a man's fitness for a particular job or in the precise words of the Civil Service 'his ability to render regular and efficient service'. It is true that in many instances medical assessment is a simple matter. Such examples as a man with one leg who is clearly fit for a desk job but not for climbing ladders or a man who has had a coronary thrombosis who is fit for a bench job but not for any heavy labouring present no real medical problems. Other conditions which may require restriction in the worker's interest are dermatitis where exposure to skin irritants may cause a recurrence of his condition; again, a man with one eye should not be working on a machine where he may be liable to damage his sole remaining eye by foreign bodies. The actual medical assessment of men with these and similar conditions is relatively simple but the practical application often carries with it difficulties with management and some moral problems for the doctor. Some managements are notoriously reluctant to engage workers with any disability whatever, their view being that any labour they employ must be entirely mobile in the interests of production. Hence it may mean that if a doctor puts any restriction on a man's suitability for employment he will be out of a job or not taken on for a particular job. On the other hand if the doctor passes him fit for all work there are the risks to a man's health which are outlined in the examples above. In addition there is the difficulty with any restriction of a particular job that this may result in financial loss to the individual concerned and some dissatisfaction with his work. This is obviously a field in which considerations other than the purely physical must apply in the doctor's assessment. Problems also arise with regard to previous illness which may constitute a hazard both for the man himself and for his workmates. A typical example of this is pulmonary tuberculosis. A heavy labouring job may precipitate a recurrence of this illness which could go undetected for a period and some of his workmates could be affected. In instances like this a good deal depends on the doctor's clinical judgment and careful supervision afterwards. One of the most important factors in resolving these problems is a sympathetic attitude from management combined with good co-operation between management and doctor.

B. *Sick Absence*

As you all know this is a national problem which in certain industries is causing great concern because of its effect on productivity. One of the main factors in this is undoubtedly the steady increase of financial benefits for sick workers originally designed to minimize financial hardship but now running at such a level as to make it almost profitable to be off sick. Furthermore, in fairness, one must remember that for a worker on a routine and boring job there is not much incentive through job satisfaction to return quickly in addition to little or no financial loss. This problem is centred mainly not on the major illnesses but in the excessive time lost for relatively minor conditions. For example, I have known a man to be off five months with bruised toes and it is commonplace to find men off for three, four or five weeks with a common cold. Apart from the effect on productivity I am quite certain that these prolonged absences are not good for the morale of the workers concerned and tend to diminish both his interest in his job and his general involvement in the community. There is no quick remedy for this problem but undoubtedly personnel departments in conjunction with the medical side of industry can contribute quite effectively to reducing sick absence. A routine but not unsympathetic enquiry by personnel departments into prolonged and repeated sick absence cases can often be helpful in at least reminding the individual that there is a job to come back to. In addition such inquiries may reveal unknown social or domestic factors, family problems and personal problems which may be a significant factor contributing to the sick absence and in some cases assistance may be given with their solution. In cases of serious illness the industrial medical officer can do a great deal to assist the individual to return to work by provision of suitably graded work. For example a man with a fractured finger may be able to come back at an early date if he is put on a job which does not require a firm grip with the injured hand. A man who has had a coronary thrombosis may return sooner if a suitable sedentary job can be found. Furthermore in some instances it may be possible to arrange a return to work for a worker who would otherwise be permanently incapacitated by arranging a complete change of job for him. This is more suitable for younger workers but in older workers one tends to avoid this particular solution because of the difficulty of teaching an old dog new tricks. It is often easier for the older worker to adapt his limited physical condition to his existing job than to learn to do a new one. Again this requires close co-operation with management.

Another aspect of sick absence is the question of medical retirement. I am quite sure this particular procedure is not used often enough in the interests of the chronically sick workmen. In the past this has been largely due to the financial implications but most firms now operate pension schemes which mitigate any financial loss. A typical example of this particularly in the North East is chronic bronchitis and heart disease which is so prevalent there. These conditions tend to be progressive in older people and a workman who struggles to work in the face of one of these disabilities may seriously jeopardize his chances of enjoying retirement or indeed of reaching it. Premature retirement at a suitable age may not only prolong life for the individual but enhance its quality. It is extremely important that this step should be accompanied by clear and tactful explanations of its reasons and should not be enforced on an unwilling worker as it can obviously do considerable psychological harm. This is particularly the case where a man may be dying of an incurable condition unknown to himself and a step such as this would undoubtedly confirm his suspicions.

C. *Job Suitability*

Lastly we come to a subject which is assuming increasing importance and which for want of a better term I will call job suitability. This is becoming more and more important with the increasing automation and mechanization of previously skilled work processes. As an industrial medical officer I am frequently met with workmen desiring a change of job for ostensible medical reasons but on investigation one finds the real cause is boredom or dissatisfaction with a particular job. This is probably more widespread than is recognized and a good deal of help from management can be given in this respect to the industrial medical officer particularly if it is identified early. I am sure this is the cause of a number of emotional illnesses such as depression and could conceivably contribute to some of our industrial discontent. Conversely one sometimes finds that promotion to a job which is within a workman's technical limits but where there is responsibility that is beyond him may produce stress and strain and eventually a nervous illness. In America a race known as Industrial

Psychologists has grown up and, though this is not common here, I think there is quite a case for a specialized branch of industrial medicine taking care of these problems.

I have referred earlier to the importance of co-operation between management and medical departments which is self-evident in a talk of this nature. I should like, however, to add two other groups which in my experience have been very helpful in the assessment of individual cases. First I have always found reliable trade union officials are always zealous in the care of the workman with the genuine problem and indeed they are frequently a great help in sorting out the sheep from the goats. Secondly the workman's own general practitioner can be extremely helpful in giving background, medical or other, information which may help to throw light on the medical and social problems which present at work.

I feel that I may have strayed slightly from my original intentions here but I hope that what I have said will give some indication of the ways in which the industrial medical officer can assist the worker in his working environment.

2. *What the State Provides*

The marriage of religion and medicine in the title of the Institute of Religion and Medicine is a particularly happy one with its recollections that for many hundreds of years a dual function of upholding and teaching the faith and caring for the sick and disabled was exercised by the church. It is felicitous, too, that the Institute should be concerning itself in this Conference with the material care available to the sick and needy in our midst. This, too, was once the function of the church and to this day the expression of 'being on the box' can still be encountered in certain parts of the country recalling that there was indeed once a parish box into which folk gave offerings in the good times and from which need was met in the bad times.

Things have changed drastically since that era in our history and I doubt if we would wish to return to what could be haphazard and widely differing depths of material concern. There is no space to give a history of the development of state care although it does make fascinating study. Perhaps I can just make brief mention of the fact that the idea of caring for the less fortunate in our midst is not a new twentieth-century concept. Poor Law itself goes back to the time of Queen Elizabeth I. There is evid-

ence of family, tribal and caste support going very much further
back in time. In our own land there is no doubt that much of the
earlier effort in the social services was against a background of
'doing good to the poor' through which people with a consciousness of superior economic and social status salved, even if sometimes reluctantly, uneasy consciences. The reluctance I have
mentioned stemmed in the minds of some folk from a correlation
between poverty and evil or, at best, fecklessness! The righteous,
they felt, very properly prospered under the personal guidance of
the Almighty.

The modern concept of social service is not like that and is
clearly based on the principle of the whole community providing
a service for each and any of its members who may need to use it.
Two men in the nineteenth century made revolutionary contributions to bring this change about as challenging as the Beveridge
Report of our own time. One was an MP, J. C. Curwen, who told
the House of Commons as long ago as 1816 of a system of social
insurance he had managed for thirty years at Workington and
Harrington Collieries in the North-West of England. Each worker
contributed 6d per week and the employer gave 2d per employee.
The contributions went to a benefit fund, controlled democratically
by a committee elected by the workers themselves. Curwen tried
unsuccessfully to persuade the House to bring in universal insurance modelled on his own scheme. The other major contribution
was that of Sir Edwin Chadwick whose experience as a Poor
Law Commissioner had convinced him that a great deal of poverty
and under-employment was caused by ill health which was itself
rooted in the appallingly bad living conditions in the fast-growing
industrial towns. The first Public Health Act owed much to
Chadwick.

Most of the contemporary social security benefits were already
in existence in 1939 when the Second World War started but
suffered from the grave disadvantage of having been brought
into being on a piecemeal basis and were not in any way co-ordinated. I have already mentioned the Beveridge Report published in
1942, and, using the dramatic idiom of John Bunyan, the Beveridge
Committee spoke of the Five Giants who needed to be slain. Disease and Want were high in priority battle order. Legislation since
the end of the war has sought to implement and amend, to take
account of changing needs and patterns, the recommendations of
Beveridge. The insured population of this country is safeguarded

against loss of income due to sickness, unemployment, accidental injury at work, contraction of an occupational disease, maternity, widowhood and retirement. These are the aims of the National Insurance and Industrial Injuries Acts. In addition there is a state system of Family Allowances providing cash benefits to families containing two or more children within certain age limits. Of important significance, too, is the scheme of Supplementary Benefits which seek to safeguard the financial requirements of those whose incomes fall below a guaranteed minimum income level. While Family Allowances and Supplementary Benefits are financed out of general taxation into which, of course, many of the recipients have paid directly or indirectly, the main National Insurance benefits are financed by the contributions of employed persons and their employers. These contributions are supplemented by the interest drawn from investments of Insurance Funds.

I do not propose to confuse you with long lists of contribution tests and other rules which govern the payment of Insurance scheme benefits. You are probably more interested in a fairly simple illustration of the sort of cash payment made. A man whose work has been interrupted by sickness could receive as a normal flat-rate[1] benefit £6 per week for himself, £3.70 for his wife or other adult dependant, £1.85 for his first dependent child, 95p for a second dependent child and 85p for each subsequent child. A man with a wife and three young children could thus have £13.35 in flat-rate sickness benefit. If his ordinary weekly wages have been over £9 per week he could also receive an earnings-related supplement to the flat-rate benefit subject to a maximum total benefit of eighty-five per cent of his average weekly earnings. The upper earnings limit for this benefit is £30 per week and the maximum supplement is one-third of the difference between £9 and £30, i.e. £7 per week. Our man with a wife and three children whose earnings we shall take as averaging £21 could have a supplement of £4 bringing his income during sickness to £17.35 per week. This supplement becomes payable after twelve days of sickness and can be paid for six months of continuing incapacity.

The patient who is injured at work would, up to 1897, have only been able to recover damages at common law and then only if he was able to prove negligence against his employer. Subsequent legislation which sought to improve the workers' lot in this respect became itself a background for confusion fraught with anomalies and bewilderment. The Industrial Injuries scheme set out to re-

move these anomalies and to put compensation for industrial
injury on the same basis as had existed for some time in respect
of war pensions. Every employed person in Great Britain is now
insured against incapacity, injury, disablement or death due to
accident at work or the contraction of certain industrial diseases.
The scheme is a contributory one paid alongside the main National
Insurance contribution. The Injury Benefit is paid for the first
twenty-six weeks of incapacity but can be followed by disablement
benefit and other allowances providing cover against special hardship, hospital treatment, unemployability, the need for constant
attendance or exceptionally severe disablement. It is the degree
and extent of incapacity which determines payment of benefit and
the Department relies upon independent medical opinion to a
very great extent.

There is no space to give a detailed explanation of the Supplementary Benefits scheme which took the place of the former
National Assistance grants. Briefly, from 1966 emphasis has been
placed upon the concept of this benefit being paid as of right just
as the other benefits I have described. The difference is that this
scheme is not a contributory one and supplementary benefits can
be paid to folk who have not been insured or alongside insurance
benefits if the income of claimants is below their requirements as
calculated under the Social Security Act of 1966. This I previously
described as setting out a guaranteed minimum income level. There
is no automatic disqualification because a claimant has savings.
The scale of requirements is agreed by Parliament which also votes
the finance required. It is in the administration of supplementary
benefits that officers of the Department can add to the basic scale
requirements by the use of discretionary powers to meet special
needs. These powers are sometimes criticized because no one can
claim as of right that a discretionary power should be exercised in
his favour. But for many individuals the existence of these powers
are probably of more value than precisely described rights because
they give the scheme a flexibility of response to varying situations
of human need. In common with those who claim a National
Insurance Benefit, those who claim Supplementary Benefit have a
clear right of appeal to an independent Appeal Tribunal and the
Tribunals can, and do, review the use of the discretionary powers
by officers of the Supplementary Benefits Commission. The dietary
needs of certain claimants suffering from various types of illness
form a background to the need for discretionary additions.

The man with a wife and three children aged thirteen, seven and four, who I described as having £13.35 flat rate sickness benefit with Family Allowances of £1.80, could be paying a weekly rent of £3 per week and would be hard put to it to manage on his National Insurance Benefit. Financial worry is not at all conducive to quick recovery in many types of illness, perhaps particularly in the whole area of stress. This man if he claimed Supplementary Benefit could have his total income brought up to £19.45 per week – a not inconsiderable help. There are, of course, safeguards to ensure that a man is not better off while he is temporarily sick or unemployed than his workmates who stay at work and thus are disqualified from receiving benefits.

Unemployment benefit is paid broadly on the same basis as the sickness benefits I have described both so far as flat rate and earnings related benefits are concerned. There is the very rewarding work done by the Department of Employment towards the retraining and rehabilitation of people returning to, or going for, the first time to work after sickness or disability. At every Employment Exchange there is a Disablement Resettlement Officer whose job it is to help disabled people find suitable employment. In exercising this function he offers advice on industrial rehabilitation to the man whose long sickness has meant he will have trouble immediately settling back into his former employment or who just cannot ever be fit enough to do so. This will involve the selection of suitable training courses within travelling distance of the man's home or in a residential setting. Suitable allowances are payable.

The Department of Employment will also give guidance on the possibility of sheltered occupation for those whose disability is continuing. A leaflet 'The Disabled Do a Good Job' illustrates some case histories involving persons with artificial limbs, one with a record of severe kidney damage and high blood pressure, one deaf and dumb, one who endured thirty-four operations on his legs in ten years of hospital treatment because of severe rickets, and many others with severe disability, all of them now in responsible work. Another leaflet 'Blind Workers' describes some of the intricate work being done by blind persons. Some of you will also know of the pioneering work of education now being pursued by the Department to ensure that epileptics are given a fair and reasonable opportunity in industry and commerce.

There is so much more I could mention if space had permitted.

Perhaps what I have said will give just an inkling that dramatic progress has been made in the care taken by the State in your name of those who, in the midst of affluence, are yet in need. In my own experience the schemes described are administered with a genuine care and concern for the recipients' welfare in its truest sense. That administration can be and is a part of both the care and the cure with which this Institute is concerned.

NOTE

1. Scale rates quoted are those current from October 1971. They are subject to review from time to time. A booklet *Family Benefits and Pensions* covers the whole range of benefits including the recently introduced Family Income Supplement and Attendance Allowances. It was issued to clergy, and others interested can obtain copies from the Department of Health and Social Security.

13 Health and Social Purpose within Industry

(1) *Peter Dodd*
(2) *Margaret Kane*

This chapter is composed of two papers given at the 1970 Conference of the Institute of Religion and Medicine at Newcastle.

The Reverend Peter Dodd is an Industrial Chaplain with the Northumberland and North Durham Industrial Mission. He has been a Chaplain in both the steel and engineering industries and is now principally associated with shipbuilding.

Margaret Kane is theological consultant in industrial and social affairs to the Bishop of Durham and in the North East. She is working ecumenically throughout an area that covers both sides of the Tyne and the Tees as well as County Durham. Her task is to provide a background of theological thinking that can support the churches' attempts to present the gospel in a way that speaks to the specific needs of the North East and its people.

1

In this chapter I would like to consider the history of industry in the North East and to use the theory, used by many sociologists and psychologists, of the hierarchy of human needs. Briefly stated, it is that as one particular need in our individual or corporate life is met, so another comes into its place, and thus there is a never ending succession of human needs to be met and mastered.

Two books on the history of the North East may well illustrate this theme. One is the history of the Northumberland and Durham Miners by Fynes.[1] Written in 1870 and republished in 1920, it is the most vivid historical document about the story of the miners during the latter half of the eighteenth and first seventy years of the nineteenth century. It deals with their struggle against oppression, which was on many occasions simply a struggle for survival. The most elementary human rights were being fought for; to reduce the number of hours that women and children under ten should work in the pit to less than sixty a week. The battle was perhaps at its most elementary on the occasions during periods of strike when the miners' families were turned out of their houses, in winter time, and were made to find what shelter they could in the hedgerows, over a period of months, while other miners from different parts of the country were brought in to do their work. It was a battle for survival and it was fought on a crude psychological level. It was a struggle upon which our society has been built. If there was then a social purpose, a social need for which was being fought, it was a very simple need; that of survival.

The second book on the same subject, out of print, is *Industrial Tyneside*[2] by Henry Moss. Written in the early thirties it was an attempt to analyse all the different social conditions upon Tyneside at that time. The obvious questions of unemployment, housing conditions, poverty and disease, were all carefully analysed area by area. If there was one overriding social need at that time; a social purpose, for instance, behind the Jarrow March, it could best perhaps be described as 'security'. The man responsible above all others for the production of this book, *Industrial Tyneside*, was Dr Leslie Hunter, then Archdeacon of Northumberland, subsequently Bishop of Sheffield, and it is interesting that when recently talking about the book, Dr Hunter said that it was planned as a comprehensive survey of conditions on Tyneside, but omitted one important area. They never thought it appropriate to consider what might be happening within the factories themselves. They never took their survey beyond the factory gates. That is now part of the history of the almost total failure of the church to speak to men's needs and aspirations in the industrial sphere. But as many will know, Dr Hunter went on to be the leading statesman of the church in righting that failure, and pioneering an appropriate ministry in relation to the industrial world.

In both these periods which these two books represent; the nineteenth century and the twenties and thirties of this century, the North East of England has had a harder history than any other region. It is true of course that no country in the world has become industrialized without great hardship. What is special about this corner of England in its story of hardship is the length of the struggle and the number of battles that were fought and lost. Because of this history it is only now that certain sections of Tyneside industry are emerging from attitudes of acceptance of the status quo which would be inconceivable in other parts of this country. If then a book dealing with the years of post-war reconstruction was to be written now, the years, shall we say, 1950 to 1975, the third quarter of the century, what would be the overriding social need and social purpose? Survival in the last century; security in the twenties and thirties; what now?

I want to suggest three particular needs not in any order of priority, because this is where I believe the theory of the hierarchy of human needs breaks down. Needs are so inter-related that they are impossible to unravel. Three needs in particular seem to be clear at this moment. First, there is a need to belong. I do not want to discuss this in terms of family or the community in the residential sphere of life, but in an industrial context. Alfred Katz, professor of Public Health in the University of California writing about 'The Social Causes of Diseases' in *New Society*,[3] talks about the importance of people living in groups. I believe this is well understood in the domestic sphere, but it is not understood from the point of view of religion or medicine in the industrial sphere. It is in fact significant that Professor Katz goes on to illustrate his theme from the family. However, the two aspects of belonging in the industrial sphere correspond with the two aspects in the domestic. There must be a sense of belonging to the primary working group and to the company as a whole, in the same way as we belong to a family and a community.

First then, what are the factors which lead to identification within the primary working group? Clearly there is an immense variety among working groups in size, structure and permanence, and there are many different levels at which a feeling of belonging can exist. Some groups work together in the same shop all day long and have obvious feelings of closeness and interdependence. Blacksmiths, pipefitters, the heavy gang who do anything and everything, 'belong' in this sense. Their job makes them distinctive. Much also depends upon the length of time that they have worked there. In a traditional industry like shipbuilding or steel, where many men in the past have expected to spend the greater part of their working life in one specific area, belonging plays a very natural part. In less traditional industries where change must be constant in order to stay in the market, feelings can be very different. I can remember the experience of one industrial chaplain, who having visited a group of electricians over a number of years had this remark made to him one day, 'Do you know, until you came here, we didn't really know each other?' The group was, of course, like many electricians, a group which only met in the department at

the beginning and end of the day, and possibly for a break in the
middle of the day. It was not, therefore, the sort of department
where everyone depended upon everyone, but what is true of the
residential sphere—that people can be associated for long periods
without knowing each other at any deep level – is true also for the
industrial.

There are many anomalies, however, in this field. Departments
which ought, one thinks, to exhibit some sense of belonging, do not
do so; and others have an almost fierce sense of belonging, in spite
of all the factors which would seem to militate against it. Forty
teenage girls pounding away at punch cards, unable to communicate because of the noise, take a brief break from this process every
hour in order to converse. Incredibly, by all accounts they 'belong'.
A hundred women working on individual cutting machines in a
relatively relaxed and free atmosphere have quite regular spells
in which the department is distinctly unhappy. In many departments this is a continuing problem which confronts shop stewards,
departmental heads and higher management. It is not surprising
that sociologists and others fall back upon the 'demonic' for lack
of explanation.

The second aspect of this sense of belonging concerns not the
primary group but the company as a whole. We are, of course, living in a period where industrial units are growing in size through
mergers and take-overs for economic reasons. Some companies,
aware of the difficulties of size, break themselves down into divisions which are autonomous. Even this, however, is not sufficient
when the divisions themselves grow to large proportions. Roger
Sawtell, writing in his book *Sharing our Industrial Future*[4] on the
problem of participation, has this to say about the size of companies: 'There is insufficient experience of high levels of participation in firms with over 500 employees, to draw any firm conclusions
about possible ways forward in such companies. Experiments with
radical forms of decentralised control would provide more experience. Self-governing dominion-status for subsidiary companies,
and federalism for separate departments in a large Works, need to
be tried out and evaluated.' Sawtell's figure of 500 employees,
which seems crucial as far as 'participation' is concerned, is relevant also to this question of belonging. Below 500, a firm can with
some justification be called a family firm, and frequently founder-
members and their families are still involved with it. Its atmosphere can be markedly different from companies employing one

thousand to two thousand. In the latter case the management finds itself quite often engineering a sense of belonging, because this is not an attribute which any longer comes naturally. It is the duty of every company to care for this aspect of its life, but I suspect it is an exercise where success will be strictly limited.

In passing it is worth noting that the erosion of this sense of belonging is an important factor in the new situation of militancy which is generally recognized in industry. A situation can arise which opens people's eyes to the fact that they no longer belong to the company, but can, if they wish, belong to the workers. A strike may appear to the outside world, according to their standpoint, as greed, madness or Communist subversion. One factor, however, is very probably operating. The workers are feeling a deep sense of belonging; to one another, to a cause perhaps, and the feeling is all the more liberating and exciting because it has not been felt for so long. There is a sense of rediscovery, of being human again, of coming home to something that should have been felt all the time.

It seems then, that we can happily belong to an association of primary groups, that is to say a grouping of different departments, but what we cannot happily belong to is an association of an association of primary groups. When that stage is reached the sense of belonging is eroded. This erosion can happen in many ways. Within shipbuilding, for instance, the attempt to rationalize wage structures and break down barriers between different crafts, a rationalization process which is both inevitable and right, it is the sense of belonging to an individual craft which is being eroded. In the past, arguments with the management have in many ways simply been the back cloth for rivalry between groups based upon craft interest. A new loyalty must now be discovered which is greater than the craft interest of the past.

In many industries, of course, the days of the craftsman have gone entirely, and semi-skilled workers predominate. It is because of this, that we move into the area of the two other social needs of today.

As I see them they are self-esteem and self-fulfilment. J. A. C. Brown in his *Social Psychology of Industry*[5] says that 'work is an essential part of a man's life since it is that aspect of his life which gives him status and binds him to society'. We can call this self-esteem, 'status'. How a man views himself in the work situation, and how he knows others view him, is of fundamental importance to his health. The erosion of craftsmanship, the dominance of the semi-skilled worker, the infinitely greater mobility at all levels lead to a great variety of threats upon a man's self-esteem. Indeed I find as an industrial chaplain that the most valuable conversations I have with managers, with foremen, on the shop floor, or when I talk to people individually, are in one way or another concerned with status and self-esteem. For many people financial reward has become the means by which to judge self-esteem, but this is, of course, a superficial judgment. Money is compensatory. As Marshall McLuhan has said, 'Money is the poor man's credit card.'

The attempt to wrestle with this problem of self-esteem must be twofold. On the one hand much depends upon an individual's maturity and his capacity to stand on his own and accept himself for what he is rather than what he does. Here the Christian gospel can speak quite naturally to individuals with great power and effect. Paul Tillich has shown us that forgiveness and acceptance are one and the same. On the other hand the structures of industrial life must be geared to encourage a man's self-esteem wherever possible. Here, in contrast, the Christian gospel, moves into unchartered territory. We have not seen the social aspect of Christian responsibility in terms of acknowledging with gratitude what others have achieved. It is sad to note how very seldom even the most elementary sort of appreciation is shown for what men and women do. This applies equally at all levels. It seems that in this respect we are all equally frail. The need on the shop floor is comparatively straightforward and obvious. What is often more difficult is the increasing number of people in positions of responsibility who are shifted into sidings in their late forties. It is not a lack of explanation which hurts; it is the implication that the loyalty, experience and initiative they have shown over the years have not been appreciated. For many there is in fact an 'occupational menopause', and they are happy to shed responsibility, but self-esteem must not be threatened at such a time of adjustment, and appreciation must be shown.

Self-esteem cannot be divorced from self-fulfilment, and here we enter the problems of job satisfaction and dissatisfaction. A. D. Lane, writing in *New Society* from his shop-floor experience, says: 'When the sociologist asks me what I like most about this job I say security. I give security top rating. Partly because I know this is intelligible to them, but mainly because I know it is useless to expect work demanding involvement. Because I know that it is an unattainable ideal to expect work that would use my actual or potential skills.'[6] This is the heart of the problem. We cannot expect work that will, in fact, use our actual or potential skills. This is where I find the motivation/hygiene theory of Herzberg[7] most helpful. Briefly stated the theory is that all the conditions under which we work (what Herzberg calls the hygiene) – temperature, lighting, cleanliness, financial reward, company policy and administration, have in the end no bearing upon the actual satisfaction of doing the job. If the conditions are bad; the shop is dirty; the lighting poor; the machines out of date; the management unenlightened, these may be reasons for dissatisfaction but if they are good they do not bring satisfaction. It is only what the worker actually does which can give him that; only those things which Herzberg calls the motivators – responsibility, achievement, work itself, advancement, recognition. Herzberg's analogy of the dustman is a good one. The dustmen take away our rubbish. By doing so they do not make us happy, but they do ensure that we do not suffer from discomfort. I believe he also applies it to the doctors, who, he says, cannot make us happy, but can relieve a good deal of our unhappiness! I suspect that the medical profession, when it is concerned with industry, is largely concerned with what Herzberg calls the 'hygiene'. On the other hand I know that the clergy, coming much later into the field in the shape of industrial chaplains, are interested primarily in the motivators; in the factors that make people 'tick'. I do, however, know of one industrial chaplain who, in his first week with a company, reported the conditions in the toilet to the Factory Inspectorate. This was not the best way to begin a happy relationship with the company. He could perhaps have persuaded the shop steward to do it instead. What does seem obvious is that any thorough concept of health must take both motivation and hygiene into account, and this is true from the point of view of both medicine and theology.

In practice Herzberg's theory seems abundantly proved in the work situation. There are many complaints about conditions, but little enthusiasm, even when company policy is impressive and there seems no ground for complaint. Enthusiasm only occurs in relation to the job itself and what it offers. On the other hand certain physical conditions can make a challenge out of a job which in other circumstances would have little to offer. Removing ice off the deck of a tanker some eighty feet high at half past seven on a February morning when there are still two hours of darkness, brings something out of people which may be unprintable but is very human. A modern air-conditioned factory cannot bring out a similar response, although the job may be similar, but neither can be called 'enthusiasm'. People in certain positions in the management structure; departmental heads, those in personnel, or on the sales side, with clearly defined briefs which suit their personal capabilities, can generate enthusiasm. Responsibility and achievement are obvious to them. What is more they have a broader perspective on the total enterprise and considerable variety in their jobs, not least in the relationships which they must foster if they are to be successful. This broader perspective and variety obviously mean a great deal to groups who move around a factory; production engineers or those engaged in quality control. The very few occasions when people on the shop floor, however, actually enthuse about the jobs they are doing, are remarkable because they are so few. A man in the planning section of a large machine shop had clearly spent all his life fulfilling a boyhood ambition working out the details of a great variety of precision jobs to the tenth of a 'thou'. It was a child-like enthusiasm; exploratory, demanding, almost eccentric because it was so rare. I was introduced to a man working on one of the launch ways in the shipyard who began to explain the intricacies of launching. I thought I would stay ten minutes, and two hours later I was still spellbound. These are the exceptions. For the great mass of people on the shop floor the job itself is unworthy of their humanity and they know it. Of course, in the vast majority of cases they adjust to it, they make friends, they find compensations, but it is compensations which they find. The drawing office, for instance, is the home of the frustrated artist, and what sense of belonging there is in a drawing office is often founded upon a common frustration. The machine shop, the tool room, the joiner's shop are all too often full of disenchanted craftsmen, and these are supposedly the places where skill still resides. If this seems too pessimistic, it is not really so, because it pays tribute to the adjustments people make and to their resilience. There is the story of one industrial chaplain who thought he would provoke a good discussion by asking the question, 'what is the worst thing about work, and what is the best?' The answer came in a flash, 'coming and going'. For that working group it was undoubtedly true, but they could laugh at the adversity nevertheless.

It is often argued that this problem of self-fulfilment is unreal as far as working-class people are concerned, because working-class ideology does not demand that a job should be a source of satisfaction. This certainly was true when survival and security were at stake. Now that, in the Western world at any rate, affluence and the welfare state have liberated us from these two needs, self-fulfilment together with self-esteem and a sense of belonging stare at us in the face. For the first time in human history a substantial section of mankind need no longer struggle to survive or be secure. This new fact must certainly colour any and every discussion; industrial, political, medical or theological. It radically alters the question, 'What is health, what is our social purpose, what is salvation'?

2

It was not so long ago that it was possible to go to an industrial area, and see the physical effects of industry upon people by just noticing the people in the streets and seeing the bent backs, bow legs and blue scars. In fact it is still possible in some places to see the physical effects of industry upon people. But it is not so possible to see the mental effects on people, the stress of industry, and the effect this has. One can look at statistics of deaths from chest and respiratory diseases, and realize that industry has physical effects upon people. But if one is trying to see the mental effects it takes a bit more thought and exploration. If we are asking in what ways people are stunted in their personality as opposed to being stunted physically by the whole environment of work in industry, this takes a great deal more thought. We are concerned with health, with wholeness, of individuals in their society, and I would like to put at the beginning the thought that the idea of health is the same as the idea of salvation, the idea of reconciliation, of the integration of people and the integration of society. The tying up of these Christian words with our whole thought about health lies at the back of what I want to say about industry and social purpose.

When I was in Hong Kong I had a group of students who were going to do a month's work in industry and before they started I asked them to sit down and write down one word which described their impression of industry. I asked them to do this simply in one word before they had had any direct experience of industry. The words they wrote down were these: dirty, soul-destroying, oppressive, hard work, unintelligent, boring, repetitive. I think this sums up the ideas people from the outside have about industry.

More than anything else it demonstrates ignorance of the true facts. The whole impression from outside is negative. And I have found this time and time again in many places. I want therefore to redress the balance. I want to mention three points, two of which are positive and one of which is negative, about the way in which industry is going. All these things are tied up with the rapidity of change, for the one constant thing about industry is the fact of change and the effects of technological change. Some of the big plants now being built in the North East – the nuclear power stations, the petro-chemical plants, and so on, will be obsolete and out of date by the time they are finished. That shows the speed with which industry is changing. The first positive thing I want to point to is the fact of innovation and the creativeness behind the constant change. I will consider later the negative side of this, but let us look first at the positive side.

The positive side of constant innovation is the necessary forward look that must be in industry and in those who take part in industry. Industry is concerned with creating a future, with looking forward, and with making innovations. People in the medical profession will readily appreciate that technical innovation today requires huge resources of money and capital investment as well as trained personnel. But innovation in industry is also taking place in social affairs, in organization, and in the way people relate to each other. How do teams work together? How do people do a job in which they are not the sole operator, where they must work across the boundaries of crafts and departments and have to get on with all sorts of other people and other teams? How does one break down the separation and get people of different crafts to work together in teams? How does one get people on the shop floor and in management to work together as a team? This is one of the big areas of innovation within industry at the moment. There are some people, though by no means all, who are finding themselves stretched and discovering a potential in themselves which would not be brought out in a community that operates in a purely traditional, unthinking way. So, the creativity of innovation is the first positive point.

The converse of this is of course a negative point – that the rapidity of change can be destructive of individuals and of communities. When one travels through West Durham one can see places where the pits have closed down, where the whole *raison d'être* of the old mining communities has disappeared. In these places one will see the negative side of change. What is happening now in parts of Durham is a reversal of immense changes that took place in the nineteenth century when the pits were sunk and when the whole district came to life as a mining area. Now, with the contraction of the coal-mining industry, whole communities are dying. Look behind the general picture to the individual, not just the workers but their families, and see the way people in the area have related to each other through shared work, and one will appreciate the destructive side of change.

This can also be illustrated from the steel industry. I know a steel foundry which is being run down as part of a rationalization plan and will be closed in about two years' time. People now working there have no future in that plant. They have been passed over in the movement of workers into more progressive plants and there is a sense of deadness, hopelessness and 'Well, what's the use?' This attitude is infectious and is being passed on to everyone who works in that particular plant.

The negative side of change is the insecurity that it produces and the meaninglessness of dying situations. Where there is change, the whole framework of many people's lives is threatened. A firm is going to be restructured, certain jobs become obsolete with new plant, new machinery. Who will go; Who will stay? How will the changes be made? There is plenty of evidence throughout industry of this kind of insecurity and the stress it places upon groups and individuals. It is insecurity which is making new groups join trade unions. Groups which never thought of joining a trade union before now look for security in trade union membership. There are breakdowns among people whose weaknesses have been exposed by change. Many people aged forty, and upwards have not got the qualifications to move into new jobs. They may have been loyal members of their firm but are now threatened with loss of their complete identity by the changes that are taking place. That makes one positive and one negative aspect of change.

The second positive point about change is that a lot of hard thinking is going on. People in industry are having to ask questions: What is industry for? What is its purpose? What are the assumptions upon which we are operating? What do we really believe about the operation we are engaged in? What is the place of work in man's life? What social function does industry perform? Is it consonant with the social aims of our society? How does it square with the Christian view of man's life in society? This debate is not taking place only within industry – it is an open debate involving people throughout the community, for it concerns the whole direction of our society. There are now fundamental choices that must be made about direction and about values. This is a positive thing and it is my experience that at this point there is the possibility of a relevant Christian contribution being made.

This is one of the things that I am particularly concerned about in the work I am doing in this region. I am working with people in industry and people in the community to enable a relevant Christian contribution to be made in this debate. It must be a contribution which is based upon a close understanding of particular situations. Industries are different and situations are different. Moreover, situations are experienced differently by people at different points within industry. A Christian contribution must be based on a deep understanding of Christian faith. This may sound obvious but there is only a thin line of understanding running through the history of the Christian church about the need for social involvement on the part of Christians and the nature of such involvement. Only a few names come to mind – F. D. Maurice, William Temple, and a few others, who really struggled with the social concern of the church and tried to see, in terms of the actual society in which they were living, what a Christian approach should be to the goals and social aims of that society, and how these could be worked out in practice. It is my opinion that a main difficulty in making this kind of contribution today is that we think too individualistically. We have not thought through the social contribution which should be made from a Christian perspective. But the way is open!

There are then many positive things going on within industry. There is much that is negative because people's lives, their livelihood and their identity is being threatened. The identity of whole communities is also being threatened for the changes are rapid and violent. But there is an open situation, in which a debate is going on about purposes, values and goals and this debate is open to people throughout the whole community.

Now I want to illustrate the changes that are going on in industry and society in more detail and suggest the kind of Christian contribution that might be relevant.

During the last year I have shared in an on-going conversation with a group of senior management people from a number of different firms and industries. In their meetings they have a continuing conversation with each other about their own concerns, and I am simply a member of the group. Some months ago the conversation took a new turn when it was stated that young people coming into industry were not motivated in the same way as older people. This was naturally of some concern to managers. They realized that different values were operating in the two groups and they decided to work through the implications of this for management styles and for industry's accepted pattern of thinking. During regular meetings over the last year we have worked out a chart which sums up our thinking on the question. On the left hand side we have listed some of the assumptions of the older people in industry. In the next column we have picked out some of the emerging values, which are held especially by young people in industry. In a third column we added any aspects of Christian belief which seemed to be relevant. Industry is based on the old style. In this money is the primary goal. Production is really secondary to this. Profits must increase for the benefit of shareholders and material acquisition is a main aim. (This is an over-simplification and there are many qualifications to be made.) In the new style of the younger person coming into industry, money is not the main incentive. For instance, I know men of the old style who go to work every Sunday, 'the firm's cats', people who are never away from the firm, who are motivated by the money overtime brings, and who do overtime whenever they can get it. But most young people are not motivated in this way. They want other things more than money. They take for granted the material things and so money cannot be held out as a bait in front of them in the same way. Now obviously there are exceptions. There is the young person who is just married and buying his house and wants all the overtime he can get, but one cannot say that young people as a whole are motivated by the offer of more overtime. There are also people in middle age who are beginning to say 'Well, why spend all my time at work? There are other things in life.' So there is a change here.

When we began to analyse what the group understood as the Christian attitude to money and to material things, we realized there was something wrong. It was all so negative – anti-money, anti-material things. The belief in the goodness of God's world was missing in the old style attitude. But the Christian understanding of the purpose of life is that God is working to fulfil purposes which include the whole creation, of which industry is a part, and that God tries to give fullness of life to all people. This is something far greater than making money and commitment to work. The acquisition of material things must take secondary place to their use in furthering the fulfilment of God's purpose. There is an open debate going on here because no longer is money seen as the be all and end all of life.

A second characteristic of the old style is that man is seen in terms of his function. He is defined by his job, as an engineer, a miner, a ship-worker, whatever it may be. But in the new style the aim is to be oneself, 'to do your own thing', to live in the present. The aim is not to 'get on', to achieve something for the future, but to live in the present and to be oneself. There is something very positive here which cannot be brushed off by saying 'young people are irresponsible'. There is a positive rejection of 'one dimensional man', the person who is seen simply in terms of doing a job, going to work. Richard Hoggart spoke on British Broadcasting Corporation television in 1970 about the changes and events of the last ten years. He said that he was surprised and was much encouraged by the way in which people have refused to be processed. The real humanity of people has fought back, and refused to be processed in terms of simply performing a function within society. This obviously ties in with the Christian understanding of people as whole people who must be treated as people, not functions. The Christian church has given support to the doctrine of work. It has provided in its teaching about life an added incentive to people to continue to perform a 'work' function in society. I am not saying that this is wrong but I am sure the 'work ethic' has been overplayed and that the idea of enjoying life, and enjoying and glorifying God has been underplayed in Christian teaching. Today people will no longer accept the work ethic as the main ethic of life and it is clear that we are in a new situation which requires new ethical thinking.

Industry of the old style spent 200 years breaking jobs down into separate pieces and we have built our society in this way, breaking people down into separate groups, so that in our cities we can say 'this is a working-class area', 'ship-builders live and work in this area', 'this is an area of white-collar workers', 'this area outside the city is the gin and Jaguar belt', and so on. It is now understood in industry that the different pieces have got to be brought together again, and this is also necessary within society. The different pieces which quite naturally were broken down in the first stages of industrialization, have now got to be related. One of the reconciling functions of the Christian church is to help the different groups in society relate to each other. Have we got the kind of understanding of Christian faith which will enable us to do this?

In the hierarchical system of organization in industry of the old style, orders came down from above. In the new style responsibility is shared and participation is encouraged. It is not easy to make this change. The system is creaking and groaning, and it is difficult to change our style. But in forward-looking industries things are beginning to happen. The church on the other hand is still working in a hierarchical way, based on the pyramid model of authority. Can the church rediscover the meaning of shared responsibility and make a contribution to society from its own experience? Have we anything to contribute to an understanding of how teams work together?

There is no time to develop other changes of thought and values which are opening up new possibilities. In the old style industry, the 'haves' have no binding responsibility for the 'have nots'. It is a competitive world and the weakest go to the wall. One has to survive and it is just too bad if other people cannot stand the pace. But today there is a new concern, especially among young people, for social justice. There is a new sense in which industry is feeling a responsibility for the whole community. 'Love thy neighbour' is increasingly being seen to include everyone and all the world.

Industry lives by change, and so does society. Too much of the thinking of Christians has been concerned with the *status quo* and with unchanging tradition, the dead past, instead of the living present. But if we delve deeply enough into our faith we realize that we are called to believe in a God who is at work in the present and not only in the past. We believe in a living, active God who is present in the changes of our world today. It is on the basis of this belief that Christians within industry and within the community have a contribution to make to the changes that are happening. If we are to do this we have some hard thinking to do about the nature of Christian faith. We have too easily accepted thinking that may have been appropriate to a past situation, without bringing it up to date.

I am not saying that technology is to be accepted without question. Christian faith should give us some criteria for making a critique of our economic and industrial life and the assumptions upon which it is based. This is urgently needed. What is happening in industry vitally affects the whole life of the community. What is happening contains both promise and threat. I believe that Christians, whether they work within industry or not, can make a contribution if they are sensitive to what is happening and if they are prepared to think with others about the social implications and the meaning of Christian belief for all life today. Christians reckon to have a contribution to make in the realm of the salvation, health and wholeness of society.

NOTES

1. Richard Fynes, *The History of the Northumberland and Durham Miners*, S.R. Publishers, 1873, reprinted 1971.

2. Henry Moss, *Industrial Tyneside*, Ernest Benn Ltd, 1928.

3. Alfred Katz, 'The Social Causes of Diseases' in *New Society*, 23 January 1969, pp.124-5.

4. Roger Sawtell, *Sharing our Industrial Future*, The Industrial Society, 1968.

5. J. A. C. Brown, *Social Psychology of Industry*, Penguin, 1954, p.187.

6. A. D. Lane, 'The Machine Minders' in *New Society*, 30 January 1969, p.164.

7. Frederick Herzberg, 'One More Time: How do you Motivate Employees?' in *Harvard Business Review*, January-February 1968. See also his *Work and the Nature of Man*, Staples Press, 1968.

14 The Care of People in Industry

H. Bernstone

Mr Bernstone is the officer of the Transport and General Workers' Union responsible for the construction industry in Region 8, and he is also Deputy Chairman of the Northumberland and Durham Industrial Mission.

This chapter is based on a contribution to the Institute's Conference at Newcastle in 1970.

The trade union interest in the health and welfare of people in industry is not new, in point of fact this is what the trade union movement is all about.

Although wages and conditions of service are the initial concern in formulating an agreement, attention is directed to the occupational content of the job, and the need for special considerations. This concern probably started with the formation of the guilds, and unions, when workers banded together to obtain better terms and conditions. Political pressure was generated, and the *Factories Acts* designed to protect women and young persons was introduced.

This measure sought to do away with 'Sweat Shop' conditions, and had a marked effect on the weaving industry and the famous 'Bryant and May' factory in London.

The unions directed their efforts along the lines of the Factories Acts, but it was soon realized that the earlier Acts did not go far enough, and that the control of 'hours of work' did little to alleviate suffering at the 'coal face' and on the 'spinning Jennies'. The unions were not a strong political force, and attention was paid to reducing the working week, and securing a wider interpretation of the Workmens Compensation Acts.

After World War I the concern for the welfare of the workers grew with the political influence of the unions, and work went on apace to determine the causes of certain industrial diseases and to set up a list of recognized industrial diseases, and the causes of these diseases. Then the work really commenced to consult with employers on preventive measures.

The progress in this field was tremendous, and even in the post World War II years, good employers recognized the need for safety equipment, protective clothing and barrier creams.

The work of the individual unions was co-ordinated by the Trades Union Congress who have their own consultative service on industrial diseases available to unions, and employers. They undertake to review the list of industrial diseases frequently, and to consult with the Ministry of Social Security on the list of prescribed industrial diseases. These lists can be obtained from any of the Social Security offices.

The preventive measures do not stop with the provision of protective clothing, goggles, etc., but include fixing maximum times that workers may be continuously employed on dangerous occupations. Strict checks are kept on noise levels, and humidity conditions, and rest periods have been introduced in certain manufacturing industries. The provision of milk is a condition when working with lead based paints, and salt tablets are provided where heat is a part of manufacture. Barrier creams are provided to exclude some of the skin diseases and certain occupations call for regular medical checks.

Facilities for washing are provided by Act of Parliament in most industries, and showers must be provided in certain of the heavy industries.

The introduction of the Industrial Injuries Act in 1948 did away with the old Workmen's Compensation Act and opened a new facet to the trade union concern for the workers, in that claims could be made in common law on behalf of workers suffering incapacity due to the negligence of an employer. Employers became increasingly aware that protection must be given when handling hazardous materials, and the various employers organizations redoubled their efforts to find the causes and means of prevention of new industrial diseases.

In the post-war years the introduction of work study and the advent of automation has brought a new problem to the fore, this is the problem of workers working on their own in isolated conditions. The system of hourly telephone contacts was introduced in certain places, to ensure the safety of operations, and patrol supervision was introduced. This does not fully meet the situation and the split shift system, where a worker works half the shift on one job and then half a shift on the other to relieve boredom, has been introduced.

The lighter view in the care of work people covers the introduction of 'music while you work', and eye-resting colour schemes. One must not forget either the introduction of medical centres, rest rooms, and excellent canteen facilities, together with method study to reduce fatigue.

The amount of information that I have given on this important aspect of industry as it concerns the trade unions is but a fragment of that which is available, for many well informed people have made a life-long study of the problems, and produced their findings in book form.

The work of the trade union does not end there, however, and the problems of benefits for sufferers of these diseases are tackled on a daily basis, and representation is given at medical appeals, specialist reports are sought and provided as a service to members. The trade union officers sit on rehabilitation boards, subscribe to Manor House Hospital, and run their own convalescent homes with competent staffs.

In conclusion I would say that the present-day problem is the one which indicates that boredom and loneliness are an industrial hazard, and our efforts must be directed to relieving the active mind, and providing a useful thought stream for individual workers. This is a tremendous problem where we all can play a part, whether it be employer, trade union welfare worker, or the industrial mission, to prevent the breakdown that appears inevitable.

15 Attitudes of Clergymen and Trainee Clergymen to Psychiatry

Alastair V. Campbell

The Reverend Dr Alastair Campbell is a lecturer in the Department of Christian Ethics and Practical Theology, University of Edinburgh. He is at present editor of the journal, *Contact*, (which is sponsored jointly by the Clinical Theology Association, The Institute of Religion & Medicine and the Scottish Pastoral Association), and is a lecturer in Ethics at the Royal College of Nursing, Edinburgh.

This chapter summarizes part of a study of the counselling methods of clergymen which formed the basis of the author's doctoral thesis.

There is some evidence of increasing co-operation between the fields of psychiatry and theology in Britain, particularly in relation to the practical training of ministers. This is shown by the formation of such bodies as the Institute of Religion and Medicine, The Clinical Theology Association and the Scottish Pastoral Association; and by a tendency in theological colleges to add to their curricula courses designed to increase the divinity student's knowledge of mental illness and improve his skills in handling the emotionally disturbed. On the academic scene, the development of diploma courses in pastoral studies in Birmingham, Edinburgh, St Andrews, Glasgow, Manchester and Cardiff has encouraged collaboration between departments of theology, psychiatry and social studies.

If such co-operation is going to increase, research is needed at this stage to determine what objectives should be sought after. Some preliminary work of this nature has already been done in the United States. Notable examples are the studies by McCann[1] and Klausner.[2] McCann surveyed clergymen's attitudes to psychiatrists, and psychiatrists' towards the clergy and their role in mental health. His study revealed some ambivalence and reservations from both sides as regards possible lines of co-operation.

(The ambivalence was more marked among the clergy than among the psychiatrists.) McCann concluded that there are serious barriers to communication existing at present between the two professions. Klausner studied over a thousand books and articles from the disciplines of religion and psychiatry which appeared to have a bearing on the relationship between the two fields, thus providing a thorough historical background to the development of religio-psychiatric co-operation in the United States over the past few decades. Other relevant studies from the American field are summarized in the survey of research by Menges and Dittes.[3] Research in this field in Great Britain is not evident in the literature.

This chapter reports a research project carried out with Scottish clergy and divinity students in consultation with the Departments of Psychiatry and Practical Theology at Edinburgh University, designed to explore attitudes towards possible lines of co-operation between psychiatry and church work.

Subjects

Fifty-four subjects were studied. They were drawn in equal numbers from the three denominations, Church of Scotland, Episcopalian and Roman Catholic. Thirty-six were final year divinity students and eighteen parish clergymen. Selection of the student subjects was made by asking for volunteers from the senior years of New College, Edinburgh, The Episcopal Theological College, Edinburgh and St Andrew's College, Drygrange, Melrose (Roman Catholic). The clergy subjects were selected by taking random samples from complete lists of parish clergy in the three demoninations within the city of Edinburgh. Sixty clergy, in all, were approached. Twenty-three (38%) agreed to participate, and of these eighteen completed the study.

Method

In order to ascertain the attitudes of the subjects to psychiatry and to the possibilities of inter-disciplinary co-operation the attitude inventory reproduced below was used.

In each of the following items alternatives are offered. Your personal opinions are being sought on these matters, there being no 'right' and 'wrong' answers. Choose the one most nearly expressing your own position on each issue. Mark with a tick the alternative you select.

1. I am not convinced of the direct relevance of psychiatry to the work of the minister.
   True...... False......

2. There is some common ground between the practice of psychiatry and church work.
   Yes......   No......

3. If 'Yes' to Question 2.
   There is a large area to be explored..................
   The area common is very restricted in scope..................

4. (a) Theology has something to learn from psychological and psychiatric theory.
   Very much so......   Possibly so......   Definitely not......

   (b) Psychology and psychiatric theory have something to learn from theology.
   Very much so......   Possibly so......   Definitely not......

5. I can think of problems where it would be difficult to say who could help more: the minister or the psychiatrist.
   No......   Yes......
   Specify

6. The minister deals with people's spiritual problems, and the psychiatrist with their emotional ones.
   True......   False......

7. My present view of psychiatry is that insufficient regard is paid to patients' personal beliefs and values (e.g. religious).
   True......   False......

8. Psychiatry has taken over much of what the church used to do in the past.
   Not true......   True......

9. Some of Church life and practice has bad psychological effects on people.
   Yes......   No......
   Specify

10. If spiritually healthy then mentally healthy.
    True......   False......

11. Perhaps I could just as happily have been a psychiatrist as a minister.
    No......   Perhaps......

12. I expect that the teaching of theology should provide me with an increase of self knowledge and understanding of my own personality.
    Yes......   No......

13. One main difference between a psychiatrist and a minister is that a minister has a call from God.
    True......   False......

14. I would like to see more on psychiatry and counselling in the Divinity Training Course.
    Yes......   No......

15. I would be glad of opportunities to take part in discussions between ministers and psychiatrists.
    Yes......   No......

In addition to this inventory, an Osgood Semantic Differential test[4] was administered, the subjects being asked to rate the concepts 'clergyman' and 'psychiatrist' on a set of seven-point bi-polar scales.

Findings

Interest in co-operation. Items in the questionnaire which suggested in a general way overlapping interests between the fields found a high rate of agreement among subjects as Table One below demonstrates.

TABLE ONE

Whole group attitudes to psychiatry (selected items)

N=54

	n	%
There is some common ground between theology and psychology	54	(100%)
Would welcome discussions with psychiatrists	52	(97%)
Can think of problems where difficult to say who could help more, a clergyman or a psychiatrist	50	(93%)
Would welcome more psychology and counselling in Divinity Course	46	(85%)
Large area to be explored between psychology and theology	44	(81%)
Not true that minister deals with spiritual problems: psychiatrist with mental problems	44	(81%)
Expects to gain self-knowledge from theology	43	(80%)

Other items in the questionnaire, however, proved to be more controversial. Seventy-six per cent of subjects considered that psychology had very much to learn from theology, while only fifty-four per cent considered that theology had much to learn from psychology. Thirty-three per cent of the subjects were not convinced of the relevance of psychiatry to church work. Ninety-three per cent considered that insufficient regard is paid to patients' personal beliefs and values in psychiatry. Forty-nine of the fifty-four subjects felt that they could not have as happily been a psychiatrist as a clergyman, and thirty per cent of subjects distinguished the clergyman from the psychiatrist by a special calling from God.

Thus it can be seen that there are limits to the subjects' desire for an inter-change between the two disciplines. They feel particularly uneasy about the handling of patients' religious and moral values in psychiatric treatment and there is considerable suspicion of any encroachment of psychology into theological doctrine (although, apparently fewer reservations about a take-over in the opposite direction!) Perhaps less surprisingly, very few clergymen see the two vocations as alternatives. The subjects' rating of the two professions on the Osgood Semantic Differential are given in Figure One. One can see that they have a more positive view of their own profession on all scales, but especially those reflecting degree of activity. The psychiatrist's role they see as relatively passive in comparison with their own.

FIGURE ONE

Semantic differential profiles for whole group ratings of 'Clergymen' and 'Psychiatrist'

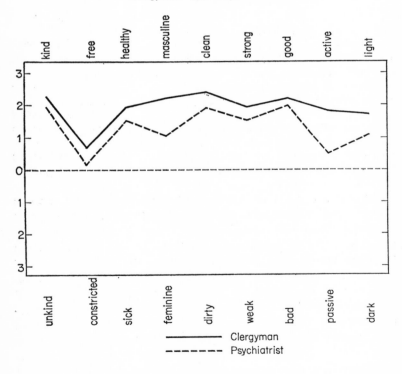

Student/clergy and denominational differences. In addition to assessing the attitudes of the whole group of subjects, differences in the sub-groups students/clergy and Presbyterian/Catholic/

Episcopalian were studied. It was found that these sub-groups did differ significantly on some items of the attitudes questionnaire.

The parish clergy were more suspicious than the divinity students of the competence of psychiatrists within the area of religious and moral values, as Table Two shows:

TABLE TWO
Student and clergy views of the handling of values in psychiatry

My present view of psychiatry is that insufficient regard is paid to patients' personal beliefs and values (e.g. religious).

	Students	Clergy
True	23	17
False	13	1

p<·05 (Value of p in this and subsequent tables from Tables by Finney *et al.* (1963[5].)

The denominations differed in attitudes to the extent that the Roman Catholic subjects drew a sharper distinction between the spiritual and the emotional, defending the former from psychological analysis and criticism (Table Three).

TABLE THREE
Differences in attitudes between Catholics and the other two denominations

The minister deals with spiritual problems: the psychiatrist with emotional problems.

	Catholics	Others	
True	9	3	
False	9	36	p<·01

Some church life has bad psychological effects.

	Catholics	Others	
True	8	32	
False	10	5	p<·01

Training. More significant, however, than the denominational and student/clergy differences was the difference made by courses designed to increase the subjects' knowledge of psychiatry and mental illness. Twenty-six of the subjects had received courses of this type during their training. The differences between their attitudes and those of the others are shown in Table Four below.

TABLE FOUR

Attitudes of trained and untrained subjects

N=54

		Trained	Untrained	
Present view of psychiatry is that values (e.g. rel.) ignored	True	16	27	
	False	10	1	$p < 0.01$
If spiritually healthy, then mentally healthy	True	2	11	
	False	24	17	$p < 0.01$
Minister is to be distinguished from psychiatrist by Call	True	6	13	
	False	21	14	$p < 0.05$
Minister deals with spiritual problems: psychiatrist with mental problems	True	14	23	
	False	12	5	$p < 0.05$

We can see from this table that introductory courses in psychiatry have led to a greater flexibility of attitudes in the subjects. They are less suspicious of the handling of values by psychiatrists and less prone to drawing rigid demarcation lines between spheres of operation.

Discussion

The findings from this study of clergymen and trainee clergymen seem to corroborate McCann's conclusion referred to earlier that barriers to understanding exist at present between clergy and psychiatrists, at least from the clerical side.[6] In the clergy studied there is confusion as to definition of areas of competence and uncertainty regarding the possibilities of practical co-operation or conceptual inter-change. Greater mistrust of psychiatry is evident among older subjects and among those of the Roman Catholic faith. (It should be noted that the smallness of the samples and the low rate of response from the clergy indicate the need for caution in drawing these conclusions. Yet it may be reasonable to suppose that those clergy who did not respond were still less sure of the possibilities of co-operation between the professions.)

The findings also point to the usefulness of (even brief) courses which discuss relationships between psychiatry and theology for modifying the attitudes of trainee clergymen. A study by Meissner[7] of twenty-six Catholic priests participating in a course in St Elizabeth's Hospital, Washington D.C. showed attitude changes similar to those reported here. With the proliferation of such courses both in the USA and in the United Kingdom, it is surprising that more research into their effects on trainees is not yet in evidence. It would seem important, at least for the theological colleges concerned, to know what ends such courses are achieving.

There are other questions implicit in this field of study which this paper cannot attempt to answer. Clearly it would be naïve to suppose that an increase in flexibility of attitude among the clergy will remove all the problems of inter-disciplinary co-operation. In the first place, the attitudes of psychiatrists to the functions and competence of clergy have not been explored; and, even supposing that all misconceptions on the part of both professions were removed, there would still remain fundamental questions as to the limits of co-operation and the possibilities of dialogue. These questions we can hope to tackle only when our inter-professional communications have been extended and improved. It remains to be seen whether, when that has been achieved, there is anything left to discuss.

Summary

This paper reports a study of the attitudes to psychiatry of fifty-four clergymen and divinity students in three denominations. The instruments used were an attitudes inventory and an Osgood Semantic Differential test. It has been suggested that:
1. Although general statements about possible areas of co-operation are approved by the subjects, there is some distrust of psychiatry, particularly in the area of the handling of patients' moral and religious values.
2. More rigid attitudes are evident in clergy as compared with divinity students, and in Catholics as compared with non-Catholics.
3. Introductory courses on relationships between psychiatry and theology result in more flexible attitudes towards inter-disciplinary co-operation.

Acknowledgements

I am greatly indebted to Professor H. J. Walton, Department of Psychiatry, University of Edinburgh and Dr Keith Hope formerly of that Department, for assistance and advice in planning of the research project.

NOTES

1. R. V. McCann, *The Church and Mental Health*, Basic Books, 1962, chaps 10 and 11.

2. S. Z. Klausner, *Psychiatry and Religion*, Free Press of Glencoe, 1964.

3. R. J. Menges and J. E. Dittes, *Psychological Studies of Clergymen: Abstracts of Research*, Thomas Nelson & Sons, 1965.

4. C. E. Osgood, G. J. Suci and P. H. Tannenbaum, *The Measurement of Meaning*, University of Illinois Press, p.000.

5. D. J. Finney, R. Latscha, B. M. Bennet and P. Hsu, *Tables for Testing Significance in a 2 × 2 Contingency Table*, Cambridge University Press, 1963.

6. McCann, *op. cit.*, chap. 10.

7. W. W. Meissner, 'Psychiatric Training for Theology Students: a Report', *Psychiatry Quarterly*, 35, 1961, pp.720–25.

16 The Temptations of Jesus

Michael Wilson

Michael Wilson, who is both priest and physician, is a Lecturer in Pastoral Studies in the Department of Theology at the University of Birmingham.

This chapter first appeared in *Christian Witness*, the magazine of Lee Abbey, and is here reprinted by kind permission of the Editor.

Other peoples' temptations often leave us cold. This is because we view a situation objectively, but we are rarely sensitive enough to enter into the inner situation within a man's heart which lures him to act against his better judgment. It is difficult too, as an onlooker, to appreciate the force of group pressures on a man. Only as a participant can we feel the responsibility for our actions, which we strive to maintain as an individual, being undermined by group feeling. The crowd which shouted 'Crucify Him' returned from the scene smiting their breasts.

'Let no one say when he is tempted "I am tempted by God"; for God cannot be tempted with evil, and he himself tempts no one: but each person is tempted when he is lured and enticed by his own desire' (James 1.13,14). Temptation is possible when the course of action contemplated both appeals to us inwardly, and is seen to be wrong. If it does not appeal to us inwardly, there is no temptation. If we do not see it is wrong, there is no temptation. Even under hypnosis we resist suggestions that are foreign to our own convictions.

These inner propensities for temptation come from at least two sources: our inheritance and our experience of life. There are aggressive families and placid families: individualistic families and socially orientated families: weakly families and robust families. To be born into one or the other is to partake of its temperament, and to be open to some temptations but closed to others: to be tempted or untempted to manipulate others, to be tempted or untempted to run away from stressful situations.

Not only temperament but also experience of life lays us open to certain temptations. The people among whom and through whom we mature, parents, teachers, siblings and friends, help us to grow in trust or distrust, in confidence or fear, and in many different responses to people and things which lay us open or defend us from temptations.

Inheritance and experience are interwoven in all the complexities of race and religion, wealth and poverty, education and ignorance. By composing our environment and shaping our desires they dictate what does, and what does not, lure and entice us. Most of this material which goes into my making is not of my own choosing, but is given to me. It comprises the supreme gift of my humanity, and the supreme temptation – to be less than human – is a temptation that presents in manifold forms. It is the content of our Lord's three temptations, the forms of which may deceive us into thinking that we could never be involved in such peculiarly messianic choices.

I think it is necessary to ask ourselves if we believe our Lord's temptations to have been real or not? Was he 'lured and enticed by his own desires'? If not, then these are just paper temptations of academic interest only. The New Testament, especially the writer to the Hebrews, insists on our Lord's real humanity and writes: 'He had to be made like his brethren in every respect ... Because he himself has suffered and been tempted, he is able to help those who are tempted' (Heb. 2.17,18).

But I suggest we usually try and evade the cutting edge of the Temptations by interpreting them at a level of form, where we can deal with them intellectually, without being either convicted or helped: or indeed without seeing them as related to problems of our own temperament and experience at all. Although the temptations of Jesus are described in symbolic language, steeped in the history of his people, and are addressed to one who is conscious of Messiahship, they are nevertheless in content the three basic temptations of man as man. They were real to him, they are real to us. To be human is to be tempted in these ways to be less than man.

These three basic temptations come and come again in different dress, to the weak and the strong, the rich and the poor. For these three temptations are concerned with relationship, and because relationship is at the heart of what it means to be human these three temptations strike at the heart of what it is to be a man. Because these temptations are so basic to humanity, so archetypal, they are open to understanding in many ways: psychologically, theologically, sociologically or developmentally. This particular attempt to understand our Lord's temptations does not therefore exhaust their meaning.

They are three temptations to distort relationship with myself, my neighbour and my God. Temptations to subtle forms of less-than-love for self, neighbour and God. They are parallel to the great commandments of Jesus to love God, love neighbour, and love self (Mark 12.29–31). As the threefold commandments are interdependent, so the threefold temptations are also interdependent. Because Jesus was a man he was lured and enticed by his own human desire. But because he was not *merely* a man he was unique in seeing the issues clearly and was not seduced. We are all more or less blind and seduced.

It is then after his baptism, when Christ has made a public act of identification with sinful man, by joining the queue of sinners for baptism, that Christ hears the words 'This is my beloved Son' (Matt. 3.17). His concept of himself is at once enlarged by a new awareness of his own identity which drives him into temptation. It is awareness that makes temptation possible: if we are unaware we just act, rightly or wrongly, without the power of choice.

A. *The First Temptation* (Luke 4.3; Matt. 4.4)

'If you are the Son of God, command this stone to become bread' is met with the reply 'It is written "Man shall not live by bread alone, but by every word that proceeds from the mouth of God".' Christ does not deny man's basic need for food and clothing and relationship. This is what creatureliness means: God made me dependent upon bread. Surely it is enough to live in trust that God will care for us food-wise and clothes-wise? But this is to deny my true self, my humanity, I am more than my body.

There is an African story told by Edwin Smith[1], about a farmer who brought home an eagle. Not quite knowing what to do with it, he put it in the chicken run, where it grew up with the chickens. One day a passing traveller saw it, and commented on its presence. 'It's a chicken,' said the farmer: 'Not so,' said the traveller, 'It's an eagle.' And he took it on his wrist and spoke to the great bird. 'You're an eagle,' he said. 'Fly!' But the eagle looked down at the chickens in the run, hopped down and pecked with them. 'You see,' said the farmer, 'I told you so. It's a chicken.'

For the next week the traveller called each day and brought such food as is proper to an eagle, raw meat and flesh. Slowly the bird's strength began to revive.

So again the traveller took the bird on his wrist and spoke to it: 'You're an eagle,' he said. 'Fly!' and the great bird stretched his wings, but when he saw the chickens in the run, he hopped down and scratched with them. 'You're wasting your time,' said the farmer, 'I told you. It's a chicken.'

Next morning while it was yet dark the traveller returned, and taking the bird on his wrist he walked a little way into the bush. As the morning sun rose and tipped with a golden light the great crag where the eagles' eyrie was built, he lifted the bird and pointed to the mountain top: 'You're an eagle,' he said. 'Fly!' And the great bird looked up to the top of the crag, stretched his wings and flew, round and round and round ... until he vanished in the sky.

And this is the first temptation, to live at the chicken level. There is nothing wrong with this for a chicken: but for an eagle to live as a chicken, is a denial of eaglehood. The temptation is to live at the animal level of supply and demand. But this is to deny my true self. Certainly I am an animal; but I am not *only* an animal. Because of my creatureliness I must have bread to exist: but to live as a human being bread alone is not enough. The words of Jesus intimate that my humanity is called into being by the word of God, fed and nourished by the word of God. My humanity is given, and the temptation is to deny this self: this self – I – who am both body, yet more than my body.

The biologist can say a great deal about me: the sociologists can say a great deal about me: the psychologists can say a great deal about me. And the chemists, physicists, anthropologists, let them all have their say: yes, indeed, the known scientific facts about me are marvellous beyond the telling of them: but I am not *only* these facts. I am more than the sum of the scientists' descriptions. My life is more than an observer can describe. I am. I do not live by bread alone. I am more than a biological creature. I live and realize my human potential through God's word. Bread is not enough; I can die amid plenty, and find fulfilment amid want. I am born from the water existence of the womb into the air existence of the world; this is natural birth (John 3.5): bread feeds me as this natural creature. But to respond to the calling of the word of God is to be born of the spirit, and to realize fuller possibilities of human relationship, and of discipleship. To deny this true self, with all its capabilities and gifts, is to deny God's gift of selfhood, of humanity, of discipleship. This first temptation, and the great commandment to love thy neighbour as thyself illuminates our understanding of Christ's words to his disciples, 'Let him deny himself' (Luke 9.23). Misunderstanding of these words has encouraged men to be less than human: has initiated a civil war, as it were, within the person: but how can a stunted and shrivelled self enter into worthwhile relationships in marriage, work, or friendship? What kind of a self do we offer in the service of others? What kind of a self do we lay down for others? What kind of a self do we offer as we take up our cross?

Deny at this point and the tempter need not come again: for in denying our self-identity, we shall be denying also our neighbour and our God. For the truth is that I *can* only love my neighbour in so far as I love myself. The great commandments are a law of my nature, not for my nature. If I do not affirm my true self, I am a sick man, sick at source. John Donne wrote, 'Sickness is a lack of self.'

A child's awareness of self identity grows in relationship to others especially to its mother. 'Me' has no meaning apart from 'You', it is 'Me' that is a child's first delight. I remember one of my small sons, in answer to my question 'Who are you?' hopping from foot to foot with delight chanting 'Me! Me! Me!' just like the child described by Gabriel Marcel,[2] who said, 'Here I am, what luck!' So the temptation to deny my true self comes first, in the same order as my personal development.

Dag Hammarskjöld wrote in his Diary[3], 'Maturity: among other things – not to hide one's strength out of fear, and consequently live below one's best.' This then is the first temptation because to say 'yes' to life is at one and the same time to say 'yes' to oneself.

B. *The Second Temptation* (Luke 4.5–8)

Christ surveys the kingdoms of the world from the mountain top. 'To you I will give all this authority and their glory ... If you then will worship me, it shall all be yours.' And Jesus answered him, 'You shall worship the Lord your God, and him only shall you serve.'

Again we are able to discern within the Jewish vision of a conquering Davidic King as Messiah, a basic human temptation to dominate others. Christ having recognized the source of his true self's growth, and accepted the immense risks of trusting in the givenness of human maturity, is tempted to deny to others the freedom which he has claimed for himself. It is the temptation – for the best of all possible motives perhaps – to dominate people for their own good. Having affirmed his own self he is tempted to deny to his neighbour an equal right to affirm his self: to deny to his neighbour the equal delight to hop from foot to foot saying 'Me! Me! Me!' with all that that might mean in terms of limitation; in the sharing of toys, and food and shelter and resources, and fears and feelings of guilt, joys and sorrows. Because again at the level of supply and demand, the acknowledgement of my neighbour places certain limitations upon both of us. Two mouths to be fed means less for me. My brother's 'me'-hood places limitations to mine. Perhaps the temptation is just that – to see sharing to the uttermost, being 'a man for others' to the very laying down of life, as a *limitation*, rather than as the secret of enlargement, fulfilment, affirmation of the other, of our own self *in* the other and of the other in our self.

From a high mountain Jesus views the kingdoms of this world, and is offered power over them. From the mountain top all men look smaller than my little finger. It is the temptation to patronize, to deal with men from a pedestal. For the parallel commandment of Christ, 'Love thy neighbour as thyself', is not some kind of ideal, but a sober statement of fact. To be human is to be thus. We *can* only love our neighbour in so far as we love ourselves. The things which we do not love in ourselves are the very things which we condemn in others. Ardent condemnation of homosexuality tells us something about the one who condemns; that he cannot love, and will not acknowledge, his own tendencies to homosexuality. The faults we object to in others are the faults that we ourselves have a mind to. My neighbour is a mirror in whom I see myself. My neighbour has an equal right to affirm his selfhood, as I have. He too is called into fullness of life, of humanity, by the word of God.

This temptation, therefore, is the temptation of the clergy to tell others how to run their lives: the temptation of the teacher to abuse authority: the temptation of the parent to manipulate children into goodness: the temptation of the evangelist to manipulate men by making them feel guilty: the temptation to hit men over the head with the Bible, binding them with texts. The authoritarian state, the authoritarian church, the authoritarian hospital, denies men their humanity, keeps men immature by denying them participation and freedom of choice. And because love must, of its very nature, make its appeal to free spirits, domination, patronizing make love impossible. 'The kings of the Gentiles exercise lordship ... but not so with you ... I am among you as one who serves' (Luke 22.25–27).

Christ grants to every man the divine right to go to hell if we wish: and without that risk, there is no chance of heaven either. Jesus stood and let the rich young ruler go (Matt. 19.22): this is not just poor evangelistic technique but follows from the meeting of this temptation. Jesus leaves the rich young man to make his own decision. At the last supper Judas's intention was known to Christ, but Judas is offered the sop from the dish: all that trembles between them in that moment is the appeal of love: it is rejected, and Judas passes out of the room under Christ's protecting silence. The ultimate test of love is its own rejection.

By respecting the dignity of man's freedom and right to choose, Jesus makes love possible, but steps out upon the way to his cross. By respecting the dignity of man, he makes maturity and true glory in personal relationship possible, and declares his readiness to pay the cost of befriending Peter, Judas, James and John – to the uttermost.

'It is written, "You shall worship the Lord your God, and him only shall you serve." ' There is little doubt that God's way with men, as we know it in Jesus (the feet washing perhaps: the mystery of the cross) kindles our wonder. Christ himself refuses to usurp power. He acknowledges its true source and displays it in his life. His life and teaching must therefore appeal to men by its own inherent authenticity. Whereas we, in our actual dealings with men, all resort to the mountain top, and bend the knee to some degree or other. We do not behave as if it was a contradiction in terms, to force men into the kingdom of God, to force men to love, to manipulate their response.

C. *The Third Temptation* (Luke 4.9–12)

Because Jesus acknowledges that power is from God, the third temptation tests his relationship to God. Within what sort of relationship is this power exercised? On the pinnacle of the temple, Christ is tempted to throw himself down: 'If you are the Son of

God, throw yourself down from here for it is written, "He will give his angels charge of you, to guard you," and "On their hands they will bear you up, lest you strike your foot against a stone."' And Jesus answered him, 'It is said, "You shall not tempt the Lord your God."'

The way Jesus meets the first two temptations assumes something very important: his complete trust in God. It is God who calls his true self into being by his word. It is God alone who is to be worshipped. And because this is the key to his resistance to the first two temptations, it is the obvious point of assault for this final temptation. As the first temptation can be regarded as a temptation to false worship of materialism, of technology, of man only as animal: and the second temptation to a false worship of power: so the third temptation is to a false worship of God. Not to a worship of someone or something other than God, but granting Christ's purpose to worship the Lord his God, the temptation is to worship him in the wrong way. He is tempted to opt for an immature dependence, rather than an adult and responsible sonship. He is tempted to a childish trust, rather than a mature trust.

A jump from the pinnacle of the temple. It is the temptation to claim for himself a special immunity. The temptation to deny his humanity, his creatureliness, the true relationship of creature to creator, of son to father. In a sense the form in which the temptation comes is a crude image – to deny the law of gravity. It comes in the form of a Jewish vision of the Messiah coming down from heaven. But it hides a typical desire for privilege, to deny that I am vulnerable like other men, and must carry this treasure in an earthen vessel. A denial that human nature as we know it, with all its limitations, is a proper vehicle for human and divine love. A denial of the fragility of human life in God's order. To deny here is to deny man the full glory of the Creator's intention, mature sonship.

And how often we cry out in our weakness, of hunger, sickness, fear, insecurity, doubt; and demand a way out of our social or personal problems by privilege, miracle or magic. Our prayers are often littered with magical expectations. But this is typical of a childish relationship. In a small group of people when the group shows an emotional dependency upon its leader, he is endowed by the members with magical powers which the group does its best to preserve.

The temptation is to adopt such an immature dependence upon

God, whereas true sonship requires the son to grow up and accept adult responsibility. In the parable of the prodigal son, the younger son who squanders his wealth in a far country returns to the father, and demands to relinquish his sonship for the relatively immature role of a servant: a request which the father not only disregards, but which he proceeds to make impossible by publicly treating him not only as a son, but as a favoured and honoured son, returned to his place in the family. The risks of sonship, and responsibility for failures of sonship must be firmly accepted.

It is the temptation to opt for a method of divine guidance which undermines the human dignity of making choices and accepting responsibility for making mistakes. It is a demand for an authoritarian God, not an authentic father.

Christ meets this temptation, and refuses to win men by irrelevant signs which would leave no room for faith. Each of the three temptations tempts him to base his ministry, and his appeal to men, on something less than love. It is a temptation that recurs to the end. 'If you are the Son of God, come down from the cross.' 'Wait, let us see whether Elijah will come to save him.' But Christ remains upon the cross, because he has denied himself any privileges which are denied to the two thieves at his side. He is with them in their common humanity, in the hour of their fragility.

The first temptation is to deny myself: the second to deny my neighbour an equal right to his self: the third temptation discloses God as one who also says 'I am'. There is a mounting evolution of perception and of priorities. Relationship to God comes last (as in the growth of a child), like the keystone of an arch which is put in place at the top to give the whole structure strength and beauty, and meaning. Though the last to be put in place, it is the keystone to the whole. Not until a man has discovered and affirmed himself, can he affirm his neighbour: not until he has affirmed himself and his neighbour can he opt for an adult sonship to God. The last temptation is the greatest, and resistance to it makes possible the putting of the 'first and great commandment' – first.

Christ's meeting of this third temptation evokes Jewish memories of faithlessness in the wilderness. Moses put God to the test, and failure cost him his entry into the promised land. Where Moses failed in trust, Christ stands firm. 'Thou shalt not tempt the Lord thy God', are words of tremendous affirmation of trust in God. The son, as he is, will not deny the Father, as he is. Jesus accepts human weakness, and a responsible and testing dependence upon God.

By opting for adult sonship himself, Christ makes such relationship possible for men. Christ's meeting of this temptation is the ultimate in acceptance of all the joy and agony of human life in true relationship of love to God, to neighbour and to self. This is man's crowning glory. This is what it means to be fully human. For this we are born and born again.

NOTES

1. Edwin Smith, *Aggrey of Africa*, SCM Press, 1929, p.136.
2. Gabriel Marcel, *The Mystery of Being*, Gifford Lectures, 1949/50, vol. 1, p.90.
3. Dag Hammarskjöld, *Markings*, Faber, 1964, p.87.